A Child's Story of the Book of Mormon

The Land of Their Inheritance

By Deta Petersen Neeley,
B.S., M.S., Ed.D.

VOL. III

Printed in the U.S.A.

By the Deseret News Press
Salt Lake City, Utah
1952

KING BENJAMIN TEACHING THE PEOPLE FROM THE TOWER

by Everett Thorpe

This book is dedicated, with sincere devotion, to the memory of Elizabeth and Jonathan Harvey Neeley.

AUTHOR'S PREFACE

The Land of Their Inheritance is the third volume in the series called, *A Child's Story of the Book of Mormon*. This book has the following characteristics in common with *The Journey to the Promised Land* and *The Precious Land of Promise*:

1. A sincere and prayerful effort has been made to present the true spirit of THE BOOK OF MORMON, free from personal interpretations.

2. For clarity and understanding, the story has been dramatized, illustrated and written in the language of today.

3. The background material has been checked for its authenticity and every effort has been expended to make it geographically and historically correct.

4. The story follows the text page by page.

5. The story is based on a carefully controlled vocabulary which makes it possible for any person or child, possessing fourth grade reading ability, to read this book without difficulty.

6. For the sake of the child's eyesight, the book has been printed with the blackest of black ink on the whitest of white paper, free from glare. The size of the print corresponds with the standard for basic fourth readers.

The Land of Their Inheritance is based upon material from the Books of Mosiah and Alma in THE BOOK OF MORMON. It is, perhaps, the most colorful, dramatic and often, tragic period in the lives of the descendants of Lehi. The people of the Lord are constantly faced with the struggle for freedom and the right to worship God in accordance with their desires. King Mosiah, through his unselfish love and devotion for his people, made a great contribution to the cause of freedom when he established the reign of the judges—thereby giving the people a voice in the government.

This was a time when great emphasis was placed on missionary work; not only among the Nephites, but the Lamanites, as well. There were many who went forth to preach the gospel; but, perhaps, the greatest of these were the four sons of Mosiah and Alma the second. After their miraculous conversion by an Angel of the Lord, they devoted all their time, bringing the people to repentance and baptism. The sons of Mosiah, labored among the Lamanites, while Alma went among the Nephites.

The guiding genius, of this period, was Chief Captain Moroni. He was a true patriot and a mighty man of God. His brilliant military strategy, won for him, many victories with a minimum of bloodshed. The following quotation describes him adequately:

Yea, verily, verily I say unto you, if all men had been, and were, and ever would be, like unto Moroni, behold, the very powers of hell would have been shaken forever; yea, the devil would never have power over the hearts of the children of men.[1]

Today, we are living in a critical time. If our civilization is to survive, we will have to humble ourselves and turn to God. One need only to turn back the pages of history to see that every great civilization that denied God, fell into decay and vanished from the earth. It is more than a little frightening to see the similarity today, when entire nations have publicly denied God. In our own great country, there is a feeling of indifference toward religion, on the part of a vast number of our people.

If the author, through the pages of this series of books, can kindle a small light, however feeble, in this darkness, then her efforts will not have been in vain.

Deta Petersen Neeley

---

[1] The Book of Mormon; Alma, Chapter 48, verse 17.

THE LAND OF THEIR INHERITANCE

CHAPTER 1

A shaft of golden sunlight fell across the palace floor and just reached King Benjamin where he sat in his huge arm chair. He rested his head against the back of the chair. His eyes were closed; but he was not asleep for the fingers of his right hand kept drumming a rat-a-tat-tat on the arm of his chair. In spite of the deep wrinkles about his eyes and mouth, he was still a good looking man. He stood head and shoulders above the crowd. He was the tallest man in all the kingdom and his faithful followers said he was the most handsome.

A patch of bright sunshine fell upon the King's left hand and drew his eyes to see from whence the warmth came. He smiled a bit grimly, when he saw how old his hand looked as it lay there in the glaring light. He closed his eyes again as if to shut out the unpleasant thought. No man in Zarahemla loved life more than King Benjamin and strangely enough, he liked old age best of all. His splendid health and keen mind made this enjoyment possible. It was a mellow time of life. He had done his share in the work-a-day world and now, he had time to reflect, wisely, upon the many things life had taught him and with the wisdom he had gained through his long years of service, he was able to give sound advice to those in need of his help. Yes, indeed, he liked old age. He liked the feel of having time to do the many things he had left undone in the early years of his life.

Today, he was not as patient as usual. It was a day he had looked forward to for many years and yet dreaded its coming. Today, he meant to give Zarahemla a new King. He had loved his people well and it gave him a heavy heart to place their welfare in another's hands.

He had sent for his three sons, one of whom he would appoint king to reign in his stead. They had kept him waiting for over an hour. He smiled to himself as he thought of his three fine sons, Mosiah, Helorum and Helaman. Mosiah, his eldest son, bore the name of his grandfather and more than that, he looked like him. King Benjamin loved and respected all three of his sons; but he felt a special tenderness for Mosiah. Perhaps, the reason for this was because he was constantly reminded of his father.

King Benjamin's thoughts drifted to life in Zarahemla. For many years, there had been no wars; not even a rumor of war. Throughout all the kingdom, there was peace and happiness. The people loved each other unselfishly and above all, they loved God and kept His commandments, faithfully. God smiled down on them and made them prosper and multiply in the land. They became so numerous that it was difficult to count them all.

In King Benjamin, the people had an excellent example to follow. He ruled them with a gentle hand

and a loving heart. In all his dealings with them, he was honest and just. Not once, during his long reign, had he ever taxed them for his support or the support of any member of his household; but frequently he gave to the less fortunate. He worked with his hands and with his mind for their betterment.

Suddenly, a shadow fell across the open doorway and looking up, the old King saw his three sons entering.

"Ah, my sons, you have come at last," said King Benjamin, smiling pleasantly.

The three men crossed quickly to their father's side and after greeting him, they sat at his feet. King Benjamin looked at them with admiration, for they were fine looking men. Mosiah and Helorum were as tall as their father while Helaman was short; but powerfully built. All three of them had dark hair and flashing black eyes.

"We are sorry to be late," said Mosiah, "but the messenger you sent, had difficulty finding us. We were visiting the sick."

"May God bless you for your efforts. I wouldn't have called you if it hadn't been necessary; but my time grows short and I have much to say to you. I have taught you well and now you, in turn, must teach your children the things I have taught you. I have taught you the language of my fathers so that you might become men of understanding and know the prophecies which have been spoken by all the good men of God. I have taught you to read and understand the brass plates and now my sons, I would like you to remember that if it were not for these plates and the commandments of God, we would have been ignorant of His mysteries. If Lehi hadn't had the brass plates, it would have been impossible for him to remember all these things and we would have lost the word of God. Oh, my sons, we would have been like the Lamanites. And now I say to you, all that you read in the brass plates and in the plates of Nephi, are true. Read them often and teach them constantly to your people, for their welfare is in your hands."

For more than an hour, King Benjamin talked with his sons, telling them over and over again of their duties to God and man. At last, when he had finished, his sons left him so that he might have quiet and rest.

It was late afternoon when King Benjamin arose from his couch, feeling more tired than when he had lain down. His thoughts had disturbed him for he remembered that he must appoint a new king at once. He knew that his days were numbered and soon, he must go the way of all the earth. It made him sad to think of leaving his people and the precious land of Zarahemla. He found great enjoyment in living and his clean, pure life made his memories rich and satisfying. He felt the full weight of his responsibility in selecting the next king. The future of his people would depend largely on the kind of king who would rule over them.

After he had changed his linen and brushed his hair carefully into place, he went to his arm chair and sat down heavily. He remembered that he had not always lived in Zarahemla; but as a small boy, he had lived in the land of Nephi. He recalled the day his father, Mosiah, told his family that the Lord had commanded him to take his wife and children and all those faithful to God's commandment, and leave the land of Nephi and seek a new home. He remembered much about their travels; but most of all, he remembered that he had been the first to see the land of Zarahemla. It was beautiful then; but it was more beautiful now. King Zarahemla and his people had welcomed Mosiah and his followers and had loved them so much that they made Mosiah king over all the land.

Suddenly, he knew that his son, Mosiah, was the one to be king. God had shown him the way and, now, he was at peace with himself for the first time in many days.

King Benjamin had Mosiah brought before him and said, "My son, I want you to proclaim throughout all this land to all the people of Mosiah and to all the people of Zarahemla who dwell in this land,

that they must come up to the Temple. I want them
to hear from my own mouth, the name of the man
who will be their new king."

"But Father," said Mosiah, with emotion, "you
are king! They want no other."

"Thank you, my son," The old king spoke, affec-
tionately. "Since my days are numbered, it is necessary that I appoint a new man to reign in my stead.
I have chosen you to be their ruler and their king.
The people will love you so long as you are righteous
and keep God's commandments. Think first of their
welfare before your own."

"Father, I am deeply grateful to you for having
chosen me king. I love our people. I shall try with
all my heart and soul to be a good king and a son
you can be proud of."

"I am not entitled to your gratitude. I did not
choose you. You, my son, were chosen by the Lord
our God. After I tell our people that you are to be
their king, then I shall give them a name which shall
make them known above all other people to come out
of Jerusalem. I shall do this because they have been
a faithful people in keeping the commandments of
the Lord. This name, I shall give them, shall never
be blotted out, except through sin. If they do fall
into sin and become a wicked people, then the Lord
will no longer preserve them by His matchless and
marvelous power. It was only through His power

that He saved our fathers from falling into the hands of the Lamanites and becoming victims of their hatred."

After King Benjamin had given his son, Mosiah, charge of all the affairs of the Kingdom, he also gave him charge of the records which were engraven on the brass plates and the plates of Nephi.

"And now, my son," said the old King, "here is the sword of Laban and the ball or compass which led our fathers through the wilderness. It was prepared for them by the hand of the Lord that they might be led according to the strength of their faith. When they were unfaithful, they did not prosper nor progress in their journey; but were often driven back and made to suffer. The Lord did this to make them remember their duty. Guard them well and be faithful to the trust the Lord has placed in you. Go now and take the proclamation to the people that they may prepare to gather at the temple."

Later, the same day, Sara and Ena, two pretty country girls, sat talking in Sara's father's garden. They had been friends since early childhood and, now, as they sat under the pepper tree, they were disturbed by the clatter of horses hoofs and the sound of a horn. Unable to see the road because of the high stone wall that enclosed the garden, they jumped up and ran to the gate. It was Mosiah, mounted upon a beautiful milk-white horse. He looked very dashing in his purple tunic and cloak of spun gold. The sight of him brought a warm flush to their cheeks and a sparkle to their eyes. Almost at once, Mosiah saw them and reined in his horse.

"Good evening, Prince Mosiah," said Sara, timidly.

"Good evening," he answered, fully aware of the admiring glances the girls were giving him. "My father has sent me forth, to bring the people a proclamation. Can I trust you to take the word to each of your fathers?"

"Indeed you can," said Sara, quickly. "When we give our word we always keep it."

Mosiah smiled at the rebuke.

"What is a proclamation?" asked Ena, at last overcoming her shyness.

"From time to time, my father, King Benjamin, has sent messages to his people; but rarely if ever, has he sent a proclamation. Now, a proclamation is like a message, except that it is a command that must be obeyed."

"I feel frightened," said Sara. "Has something terrible happened—a war or something?"

When Mosiah answered, his voice was gentle and reassuring. "There is no reason to be frightened. King Benjamin has asked me to tell the people to gather at the Temple. Will you ask your fathers to bring their wives, their daughters, their sons and their children's children, until the entire family has been gathered together? That is all of the proclamation. My father will tell you his message when you reach the Temple."

Bidding the girls good-bye, Mosiah rode off down the lane, rolling up great clouds of dust as he went. Soon, he was completely hidden from view and the girls went back to sit on the bench beneath the pepper tree. They talked of the mysterious proclamation and about the handsome prince.

CHAPTER 2

"Father!" shouted Helaman, coming into the great hall of the palace.

"Here I am, son," said King Benjamin from where he sat reading, at a small table, close to the window.

"Mosiah is back!" said Helaman, excitedly. "Already, the people are gathering at the Temple."

No sooner had Helaman spoken than Mosiah burst into the room, looking tired and dusty.

"Welcome home, my son," said the old King.

"I planned to be back before this. I made the journey in good time; but on the way back, I had to ride carefully as the roads were all crowded with our people, their donkeys and the best of their flocks. Oh, it's quite a sight, Father."

"Why should they bring their flocks?" asked Helaman.

"Your brother said the best of their flocks and they bring them so that they might offer them to God, as a sacrifice, according to the Law of Moses. And you, Helaman, are to select the best animals in our flocks so that we, too, might offer them to God in thanks for His mercy and goodness. Mosiah, how did you find our people?"

"There is peace and happiness throughout all the land. They are a faithful people, loving each other and God," said Mosiah.

"Already," said Helaman, "there are more people than our temple will hold and yet they continue to come."

Benjamin's smile was warm and a bit mysterious as if he knew something they didn't know. Finally, he drew them to the window and said, quietly, "You can see the temple from here. Look, do you see anything new?"

"A tower!" said both sons at once.

"I had it built so that most of my people will be able to hear the sound of my voice. However, even then, some will not be able to hear me, so I am having my words written down in order that they can read my message."

Great admiration shone in the eyes of Mosiah and Helaman. How wise and clever their father was; making his plans and carrying them out even before anyone else had even thought of it.

When the people were all gathered at the Temple, they pitched their tents so that each door was toward the Temple. This was done so that they might stay in their tents and hear the words of King Benjamin. When the King began to speak, the people felt their faith being strengthened for they knew he was inspired by the Lord. He taught them many things, too numerous to be written.

"I have worked with my hands," said the King, "in order to serve you, that you might not be burdened with taxes. I tell you these things that you may learn that when you are in the service of your fellow men, you are really in the service of God. He has created you and all that you have, you owe to Him. Yet, for all His goodness, He asks nothing except that you keep His commandments. He has promised that, if you will keep His commandments, you shall prosper in the land.

"I have asked you to gather at the Temple to tell you that I can no longer be your teacher and your King. Even now, as I stand here, my whole body trembles; but the Lord God will support me for He has commanded me that I should tell you that my son, Mosiah, is a King and ruler over you. And now, my people, I want you to do as you have always done. You have kept my commandments and the commandments of my father and now I ask you to keep the commandments of my son, or the commandments of God which shall be delivered to you by Mosiah. Do this and you will continue to prosper and your enemies will have no power over you."

King Benjamin continued to speak to the people from the tower, pouring out words of wisdom and words that sank deep into men's hearts, making them search their souls for hidden sins.   He told them about a wonderful thing that had happened to him. One night, an Angel of God came and stood before him and told him to awake and listen carefully to all that he had to tell him. The Angel said that after a period of time had passed away, Jesus Christ, the Son of the Lord our God, would come to earth and His spirit would dwell in a human body. Then he told King Benjamin of the marvelous miracles Christ would perform—he would make the blind to see, the deaf to hear and the dead to live again. The Angel pictured how Christ would suffer, bleed and die, and then, most glorious of all, he would arise from the dead and go among the people. Because of His death and resurrection, men would be given eternal life if they would but keep the commandments of God.

King Benjamin, suddenly, stopped speaking and looked down at the multitude. He saw that all those within the sound of his voice had fallen to the earth for fear of the Lord.

They cried aloud with one voice, saying: "Oh, have mercy and forgive us for we believe in Jesus Christ."

After they had spoken these words, the spirit of the Lord came upon them and their hearts were full of joy. King Benjamin stood, for a long time, looking down from the tower upon his people below.

He was very tired. It had taken great effort to talk for such a long time and only through God's support, had he been able to accomplish it. He stood enchanted by the picture his people made. Their brilliant colored tents, spread out against a backdrop of green trees, completely encircled the Temple. The bright sunshine caught up the colors and made them dazzling to the eyes. These were his people; peace-loving and kind to one another. Suddenly, his eyes filled with tears as he thought that, perhaps, this would be the last time he would speak to them. He wondered if they had believed his words. For their own sakes, they must believe. In order to find out the truth, he sent among them and asked them.

With one voice, they answered: "Yes, we believe all the words spoken by our King. Furthermore, we believe the words the angel spoke to him regarding the coming of Christ. From this day forth, we will forsake our sins and always do good. We promise God to keep His commandments and be obedient to Him in all things."

Now, these were the words that King Benjamin hoped to hear for he had promised to give his people a name that should never be blotted out, as long as they kept God's commandments. But he couldn't give them the name until they believed in Christ. Joy filled his heart as he began to speak once more: "From this day forth, you shall be known as THE CHILDREN OF CHRIST. You are now His sons and daughters for He is the Father of your spirits. If you keep the promise you made to God, you will one day find yourselves at His right hand in Heaven."

After King Benjamin had finished speaking to his people, he decided it would be wise to record all the names of those who had taken upon them the name of Christ and promised to keep His commandments. Great joy filled the old King's heart when he discovered that every person in the kingdom, except young children, had his name recorded. King Benjamin had his son, Mosiah, brought before him. He blessed Mosiah as king and ruler over the people. Besides giving him the kingdom, he made him the keeper of the records. Next, he appointed priests to go among the people to teach and constantly remind them of their vows to God. Mosiah was thirty years old when he became king. It had been 476 years since Lehi had left Jerusalem.

Three years later, when the air was mild and fragrant with springtime blossoms, King Benjamin died. He died as he had lived, with simple dignity and at peace with God and man. As his three sons, Mosiah, Helorum and Helaman, stood looking down at their father for the last time, they thought he looked years younger. A faint smile just touched his lips.

"Our father was a great man," said Mosiah, quietly.

"Indeed, he was," said Helaman. "No man ever deserved a richer reward."

"I was thinking, as I stood here looking at him, that perhaps, he was already being rewarded. The expression on his face is an inspiration. He looks so happy that I find my belief in the hereafter strengthened," said Helorum, deeply moved.

Chapter 3

King Mosiah walked in the ways of the Lord, keeping all His commandments, faithfully. He had great strength of character and his sincere love for his people made him place their welfare above his own. He believed it was good for them to work with their hands as well as their minds. Furthermore, he believed that the closer they worked with nature, the closer they came to God. Because of these things, he encouraged them to till the soil and to raise flocks and herds.

Now, Mosiah would not ask his people to do the things he himself would not do, so he, too, tilled the soil and used his hands in many ways. Mosiah supported himself and his family, just as his father had done. He didn't want his people to be burdened with taxes. He wanted every person to enjoy complete freedom.

The first three years of Mosiah's reign, were happy, peaceful ones; but then, one day, a group of people began talking about Zeniff and the men he took with him to the Land of Nephi. Now, this had happened many years before, when Mosiah's grandfather had been king. After Zeniff and his followers left Zarahemla, they were never heard of again. Finally, King Mosiah became tired of their teasing and appointed sixteen strong men to journey up to the land of Lehi-Nephi and discover what had become of them.

The very next morning, they set out upon their journey. Their leader was a strong and mighty man named Ammon. He was a descendant of Zarahemla. They did not know the right course to follow in order to reach the land of Lehi-Nephi and, for that reason, they wandered in the wilderness for forty days. In the midst of their wandering, they came to a hill, which is north of the land of Shilom.

"We will pitch our tents here," said Ammon.

"Are we near the land of Nephi?" the men asked him.

"All I know is that we are lost," said Ammon. "I want to leave you here, where you will be safe, until I locate the land of our inheritance."

Ammon took three of his brethren with him and set out immediately. They hadn't gone far when they came face to face with a man.

"Who are you?" they asked.

"I am King of the people in the land of Nephi and in the land of Shilom."

Without any warning, Ammon and his men were, suddenly, surrounded by the King's guards who took them and bound them securely and threw them into prison. When they had been in prison two days, the king had them brought before him and the bands that held them were loosened.

"I have had you brought before me to answer a few questions. Perhaps, you should have been put to death at once; but I decided to give you this chance. You see, I like your courage. Behold, I am Limhi the grandson of Zeniff, who came up out of the land of Zarahemla to inherit this land." As he spoke, he watched them carefully, "I want to know why you were so bold as to come near the walls of the city, when I, myself, was with my guards outside the gate."

When Ammon saw that he was permitted to speak, he went quickly to the king and bowed low before him, saying, "Oh King, I am very thankful to God that I am alive and can speak. I will speak with boldness for I am sure that if you had known me, you would not have bound me. I am Ammon, a descendant of Zarahemla. We have come up out of the land of Zarahemla to ask about our brethren, whom Zeniff brought from our land."

As King Limhi sat listening to the words of Ammon, a warm flush of pleasure lit up his face and he said, "Now, I am convinced that my people, in Zarahemla, are still alive. My joy is great and tomorrow, my people shall rejoice. We are in bondage to the Lamanites and they tax us heavily. We know that you will deliver us out of the hands of the Lamanites and we will be your slaves. It will be better to be the slaves of the Nephites, than to pay tribute to the Lamanites."

Limhi called his guards and commanded them to set Ammon and his men free. He told them to go to the hill, which was north of Shilom, and bring the rest of the men to the city so that they might eat and drink and rest themselves from their long journey. When this was done, King Limhi sent out a proclamation among all his people, asking that they gather at the Temple so that he might speak to them.

The next day, when his people were gathered at the Temple, Limhi said: "Lift up your heads and be comforted for the time has come when we shall no longer be in bondage to our enemies. You know how we are burdened down with heavy taxes. We are forced to pay, to the king of the Lamanites, one half of all the grain we raise. One half of the increase of our flocks and herds. One half of all else that we possess. If we refuse to pay, we lose our lives. It is no wonder that you, my people, are sad. Many of our brethren have been killed and their blood has been spilled in vain all because of sin. If the people had not sinned, the Lord would not have let this great evil come down upon us. God has been very angry with us and, in his wrath, he let our enemies come upon us. The Lord promised this people that if they continued in sin, He would destroy them and He has fulfilled His promise. But, behold, He has also told us that if we return to Him and serve Him faithfully, He will, some day, deliver us out of bondage."

King Limhi told them many things and the

people listened, eagerly. He told them about their brethren in the land of Zarahemla. Then he had Ammon stand up before the multitude and tell them all that had happened in the land of Zarahemla, from the time that Zeniff left, until he, himself, came to the land of Nephi. When Ammon had spoken, King Limhi dismissed the multitude.

When all the people had gone to their own homes, King Limhi and Ammon started toward the palace. At first they walked in silence, each one busy with his own thoughts. Ammon was thinking of Zarahemla; of its peace and quiet and most of all, of the happy people. Here, in the land of Nephi, there was a feeling of unrest. Because they were in bondage to the Lamanites, they were an angry, sorrowful people. And, now, in the dusk of early evening, everything took on a strange look. The deepening shadows gave him an uneasy feeling.

"Ammon, can you read strange languages?" asked King Limhi.

"No, but why do you ask?" questioned Ammon.

"That is a long story; but I will tell you, briefly. Sometime ago, I felt sore at heart when I saw how my people suffered because of the Lamanites and wanting to free them, I sent 43 men to the north, in search of our people, who lived in the land of Zarahemla. I felt sure that, when they heard of our misery, they would come to our rescue."

"What became of the men?" asked Ammon, with sincere interest.

"They became lost. However, they found a land of many waters and in this land, they found the bones of men and beasts and the ruins of mighty buildings. They brought back with them, among other things, 24 plates of pure gold. There is strange engravings upon them and since no one in my kingdom, can tell me what they say, I am very anxious to find an interpreter. Do you know such a person?"

"Yes, indeed I do," said Ammon. "He is our Prophet and Seer. God has given him a rare gift with which he can translate and interpret all languages. This instrument is called an interpreter. It is a gift that God gives only to choice men of the land."

When King Limhi heard Ammon's words, his heart was filled with joy and he gave thanks to God.

"There is no doubt, a great mystery contained in these plates. These interpreters were, undoubtedly, prepared for the purpose of revealing such mysteries, to the children of men," said King Limhi.

Early next morning, King Limhi had the plates brought to Ammon. These were the records of his people from the time Zeniff and his followers had come out of the land of Zarahemla. Ammon read the records with eagerness. At last, he was to know just what had befallen his brethren.

The first part of the record, written 80 years

before, told of things already known by Ammon. It was an account of the first group of men to leave Zarahemla. Their leader had been a quarrelsome man and because they forgot the Lord, they let him stir them up until they shed each other's blood. Zeniff and the others, who had not been killed, returned to Zarahemla. Zeniff gathered together a large group, who set out once again, for the land of Nephi. After many hardships, they came to the land of Shilom and here on the hill, they pitched their tents and waited while Zeniff and four strong men entered into the city of Lehi-Nephi. They went to speak to the Lamanite king, whose name was Laman. He was just as cunning and sly as the first Laman, that lived hundreds of years before. Now, Laman and his people were lazy and, at times, when they had neglected tilling the soil, there was famine in the land. Therefore, he smiled at Zeniff and offered to enter into a treaty with him, whereby the Nephites would be given back the land of their inheritance. Furthermore, they were to be given the land of Shilom. Immediately, the Lamanites withdrew from the land and the Nephites moved in. They set to work, repairing the walls about the city and building new buildings. Soon, the city of Shilom and the city of Lehi-Nephi began to be beautiful once more. They tilled the soil and raised flocks and herds and because they loved God and kept His commandments, they prospered and multiplied.

Twelve years passed and Zeniff and his people grew stronger, day by day. King Laman watched them with growing uneasiness. It had been his plan, from the first, that as soon as they became prosperous, he would bring them into bondage, so that the Lamanites might glut themselves with the riches of the Nephites. Therefore, in the thirteenth year of Zeniff's reign, in the land of Nephi, the Lamanites came upon the people while they watered their flocks and began to slay them, taking their animals and their grain. When Zeniff heard about their treachery, he asked God for guidance and strength. Since the Lamanites far outnumbered the Nephites, King Laman felt very bold. They had forgotten God, long ago, so they did not know His power. God answered the prayers of His people and made them so mighty that they killed ten Lamanites for every Nephite until, at last, the Lamanites were driven out of the land. Once more, Zeniff and his people began to prosper. For 22 years, there was peace and happiness; but at the end of that time, the Lamanites made war upon them once more. Their hatred for the Nephites was black and terrible to see. Since the time Lehi left Jerusalem, their hatred had grown and had been passed on to their children for four hundred years. They blamed the Nephites for all their misfortunes. Zeniff and his people, were well prepared for them and once again, they drove them

out of the land. Zeniff grew old and died and his kingdom was passed on to his son, Noah.

It was a dark and tragic day for the people, in
the land of Nephi and Shilom, when Noah became
king over them. He was wicked and hard-hearted,
caring only for his sinful pleasures and comforts. He
knew his people were prosperous; that they lived in
beautiful homes and that many of them had gold and
silver and precious stones. When he saw them in
their fine clothing, he became greedy and wanted
what they had, so he appointed high priests to help
him tax the people. They took one fifth of all their
possessions. Then King Noah set to work, planning
great buildings for his workmen to build. First, they
built a palace for the king and his many wives. His
throne was made of the finest wood and decorated
with gold, silver and precious gems. The seats which
were set apart for the high priests, were higher than
all the other seats and decorated with pure gold. A
breastwork was built before each seat so that they
might rest their arms, while speaking. A great
tower was built, near the Temple. It was so high
that from it, one could see the land of Nephi, Shilom
and even Shemlon, the land of the Lamanites. The
Nephites planted grapes and spent much time in
making wine and adding drunkenness to their other
sins. The people worked hard to support King Noah
and his priests in their laziness and sinful ways.
They forgot God and thought only of their own great-

ness, boasting that fifty of their men could stand against thousands of Lamanites.

There was a man, in the kingdom, that watched with sorrowful eyes and a heavy heart, while King Noah and his wicked priests, led the people into sin. Even the best of the people, no longer knew God or kept His commandments and so, Abinadi, for that was the man's name, began going among the people, secretly teaching them. God saw his work and was pleased. Now, Abinadi, was strong in body and quick in mind, so God made him His prophet. After a while, King Noah heard of his prophecies and had his guards seek him out and bring him before the throne. Abinadi was unafraid and spoke plainly before the king and his priests. He told them that the sin they lived in, was unforgiveable in the sight of the Lord. Furthermore, he told them that unless they repented and turned to God, they would be visited with pests, all manner of diseases, famine, terrible storms, and wars, wherein much blood would be shed. He told them, too, that they would become as beasts of burden, having packs lashed to their backs and driven before their masters. So great was King Noah's anger, that he had him turned over to the priests to decide his fate.

From among the priests, a young man came and stood before the king. This man was Alma, a descendant of Nephi. He began to plead with the king to spare Abinadi's life. He had heard all the words

spoken by the old prophet and he knew that he had
told the truth. Alma knew that he and his people
were wicked. As King Noah listened to Alma's pleading, he grew very angry and ordered him out of the
kingdom. Then, as soon as Alma had gone, the
wicked king sent his army after him to kill him.
Alma ran as fast as he could and hid himself away
so that the king's men could not find him. He remained hidden for several days, writing all the words
that Abinadi had spoken.

As soon as Alma had gone, the king ordered his
guards to surround Abinadi and cast him into prison.
After three days, King Noah had him brought before
him.

"I have brought you to me," said the king, "to
give you another chance. If you will deny your
prophecies and also take back your words about our
wickedness, I will set you free."

"That I will never do," said Abinadi, in a firm,
clear voice. "All that I have spoken, is true."

When the king heard these words, he ordered
Abinadi to be burned alive. While the old prophet
suffered the agonies of burning, he continued to
prophesy; telling the king that he, too, would be
destroyed by fire. But the sinful king and his cruel
priests only laughed and mocked him.

CHAPTER 4

"I hope I am not disturbing you," said King Limhi, coming into the room where Ammon sat, reading the record.

"Do come in," said Ammon. "I can read later."

"No, I won't disturb you. I know how anxious you are to learn the history of our people." With these words, he walked out of the room and Ammon turned back to the records and continued to read about Alma.

Alma repented of his sins and went among the people, secretly, teaching them the words of Abinadi. Many of his people believed him and those who did believe, went to a place called Mormon. There was, in Mormon, a fountain of pure water and since there was a thicket of small trees nearby, Alma hid here, in daytime, from the searchers of the king. Many of his followers came to hear his words. After teaching the people the way to enter the Kingdom of Heaven, he began to baptize them. They were called the Church of God.

Alma appointed priests to teach the people. He told them there must be no quarreling. They must have a single purpose; the teaching of God's word. There was one day, in each week, set apart to worship God. The priests were not to depend upon the people to support them; but for their labor, they were to

receive the grace of God. Alma commanded that each
one give according to his possessions and to those
who had nothing, help must be given. They must
give of their own free will and good desires toward
God. This was to support the needy. All their meet-
ings were held in Mormon, in order that King Noah
would not learn of their whereabouts. They knew
that he would surely destroy them if he found them.
But, behold, the king had already discovered that
many of the people, had moved out of his kingdom.
He sent his servants to watch them. Therefore, on
the day, they gathered to worship God, King Noah
discovered them. He sent an army to destroy them.
Alma, being alert, discovered what the king intended
to do, so they took their tents and their families and
fled into the wilderness. There were 450 souls.

The king's men looked everywhere for the people
of the Lord; but without success. Finally, they gave
up the search and returned to the land of Nephi.
They were frightened that the king would be angry,
when they came back empty handed. Perhaps, he
would even kill them. However, they were greatly
surprised when they found the king waiting for them.
He was glad to have them back because there was
rebellion in the kingdom. The larger part of the
people remained loyal to King Noah; but a small
group had openly expressed their unwillingness to
support a king who taxed them heavily and used their
labor to support him in his wickedness.

Now, the leader of this smaller group was named Gideon. He vowed that he would rid the people of the evil king. He drew his sword and went to find King Noah. When the two men had fought a short time, King Noah saw that Gideon meant to kill him, so he gathered up his royal robes and ran as fast as he could go. He ran and ran until he reached the very top of the tower. Gideon ran after him as fast as he could go. When the king saw that he was running after him, he began to plead with him to spare his life. Then casting his eyes about for some place to hide, he saw to his horror, that the Lamanites had gathered their armies and were, even now, entering the land of Nephi. Gideon, who had reached the top of the tower, turned his eyes toward the place where King Noah was pointing, with a trembling finger.

"The Lamanites are coming to kill us," said King Noah. "This is no time for us to fight each other; but to unite our forces and flee from the land."

"I agree with you," said Gideon. "I shall deal with you later."

King Noah commanded the people to take their wives and children and flee from the Lamanites. But the Lamanites ran after them and overtook them and began to kill them. When King Noah saw what was happening, he ordered the men to leave their wives and children and flee before the Lamanites. Many of the men refused to leave their families, saying that they would rather perish. Then they asked their fair

daughters to stand before the Lamanites and plead
with them to save their people. The Lamanites were
charmed by the beauty of the Nephite women. In fact,
they were so impressed by their pleading that they
decided to spare their lives. They took them captive
and carried them back to the land of Nephi, telling
them they might possess the land on one condition.
They must deliver up King Noah into their hands.
Furthermore, they must give the Lamanites one half
of all they possessed and continue to do this from
year to year.

It was not long before the king of the Lamanites,
discovered that among his captives, was Limhi, one
of King Noah's sons. He was not at all like his father.
He was kind and just. Now, Gideon knew that Limhi
would not destroy his father, although, he was aware
of his evil deeds. Gideon was determined that King
Noah and his priests should pay for their crimes,
so he sent men to overtake them, in the wilderness.
They had not gone far, until they came upon the men,
who left their wives and children, to flee with King
Noah.

"Where are the priests and King Noah?" asked
Gideon's men.

"We destroyed King Noah by fire. We wanted
to return to the land of Nephi and when King Noah
commanded that we stay with him, we grew very
angry and destroyed him. We would have destroyed

the priests; but they ran away," answered one of the men.

When they reached the land of Nephi and brought the news of King Noah's death, they appointed Limhi to be their King. He began, at once, to establish peace. The Lamanites withdrew from the land of Nephi; but the king put a heavy guard about the land so that the Nephites could not escape. The Lamanites were happy, at the prospect of living upon the labor of the Nephites. They would not have to work and could spend all their time, hunting and fishing. For two years, Limhi and his people lived in peace with each other and the Lamanites.

One day, a terrible thing happened. It had been the custom of the Lamanite girls, to go to a place in Shemlon, to dance and sing and enjoy themselves. One day, the wicked priests discovered them. They hid themselves and watched them dance. Each day, after that, they continued to watch until at last, when there was a small group, they came out of their hiding place, captured the girls and carried them away into the wilderness.

When the Lamanites found that twenty-four of their daughters were missing, they, immediately, blamed Limhi and his people. With terrible anger, they began to prepare for war. Fortunately, Limhi saw their preparations from the tower and because they were few in number, compared to the Lamanites, he hid them away where they would not be seen.

When the Lamanites came, the people of Limhi, fell upon them and killed them. At last, the people of Limhi began to drive the Lamanites before them.

When the Lamanites were driven from the land, King Limhi, and his people, found the king of the Lamanites, lying in a field, with the dead. He was not dead; but only wounded. They bound up his wounds and took him to King Limhi, saying, "Oh King, we have brought you the king of the Lamanites. Let us slay him."

"No," said King Limhi. "There has been enough bloodshed, already," and then, turning to the king of the Lamanites, he said, "Why did you break your word? Surely, you remember the oath you gave me that you would not come upon us in war, if we would pay you half of all we possess. We have kept our word and yet, you have broken yours."

The king of the Lamanites grew very angry and said, "I have broken my word because your people have carried away the daughters of my people. I grew so angry, that I went before my army and led them in war against you."

Now, King Limhi had heard nothing of all this and he, too, grew angry when he heard what his people had done. Immediately, he commanded that they search the homes, for the Lamanite daughters, and punish the guilty.

When Gideon heard about the search, he said to the king, "I pray thee, wait. Do not search the people, for they are free of guilt. Don't you remember the wicked priests of your father, Noah? They are in the wilderness and they are the ones who have stolen the Lamanite daughters. Oh king, tell the king of the Lamanites, so that he will be satisfied for even now, the Lamanites are returning to make war upon us and you know that we are few in number, compared with them. Let us make peace, while there is yet time, for surely all the words of Abinadi are coming true. If we had only listened to the words of God, and turned away from sin, then we would not be suffering as we are, today."

King Limhi turned his kindly eyes upon Gideon and thanked him for his wisdom. And when he had told the king of the Lamanites about the wicked priests and that they must be the guilty ones, the king of the Lamanites said, "Let us go forth without weapons, and meet my people. I give you my promise that they will not kill you."

When the Lamanites saw that the people of Limhi were without weapons, they took pity upon them and returned with their king, in peace, to their own land.

King Limhi was both grateful and happy to have peace. His people were very dear to him and he grieved for those who had been killed. After a while they took new heart in their work; but there were dark days ahead for them. It was well, they didn't know how great their suffering was to be, or they may have welcomed death.

In a short time, the Lamanites began to stir up their anger against the Nephites. They did not dare kill them because the king had given his word. But they went into the borders of the land, where the Nephites worked in the fields and, without warning, they would strike them on their cheeks and put heavy loads upon their backs and drive them as though they were dumb animals. Their suffering was great and there was no way they could escape. The Lamanites had them completely surrounded on every side. When they could stand it no longer, they went to their king and asked if they might go to war against the Lamanites. Limhi hated war with all his heart and soul; but at last, he gave them permission to go into battle. But their enemies were victorious. They were beaten so badly, that the cries of the mourners, could be heard throughout the land—wives mourning for their husbands, mothers for their sons, sisters for their brothers. At sight of so much grief, Limhi let them go into battle a second and third time. But each time, they were beaten and their suffering became terrible to see. The Lord's word was fulfilled. They began thinking about Abinadi and his promise that if they would turn to God, he would help them. They humbled themselves, even to the dust, and submitted to the yoke of slavery, allowing themselves to be beaten and driven to and fro, according to the wishes of their enemies. They began to cry, to God, for help. So great were their cries that they lasted all day long. The Lord was slow to hear them because of their sins. Finally, he heard them and began to soften the hearts of the Lamanites, so that they made their burdens lighter. In a small way, they prospered so that, now, they were not always hungry.

The king did not dare trust himself, outside the walls of the city, unless he took his guards with him, fearing that he might fall into the hands of the Lamanites. It was here that Ammon and his men found the king.

CHAPTER 5

After Ammon had finished reading the record of Zeniff and his people, he sat for a long time, thinking of many things. In all that had happened to the people, there was one thing that stood out clearly— as long as they kept the commandments of the Lord, they prospered and were happy. Even, after they fell into sinful ways, the Lord had been slow to anger and continued to let them prosper, for a time. While the Lord had been slow to anger, yet He was just as slow to forgive. However, of late, He began to soften the hearts of their enemies by making their burdens just a little lighter. All at once, an idea flashed through Ammon's mind—an idea so simple and yet so startling, that it brought Ammon erect in his chair. Suddenly, the thought came to him that God was using him as an instrument to bring freedom to Limhi and his people. It all seemed very clear to him now. For a long time, while at Zarahemla, he had been thinking of the people, that went with Zeniff many years before and were never heard of again. He just kept thinking of them and pleading with his king, Mosiah, to let him go in search of them. At last, the king gave him permission to take sixteen strong men and go in search of them. Now, he knew there had been some force, stronger than himself, that led him to do these things. The Lord had worked in a mysterious way his wonders to perform.

Through the open window, came the cries of women and children, weeping for their dead; the cries of the suffering people, bearing burdens too great for them; and the cries of all the people, pleading with God for forgiveness and mercy. Their cries touched Ammon's heart and he went in search of Limhi.

"Oh, there you are," said Ammon, coming upon Limhi just outside the palace.

Ammon talked to Limhi about ways of freeing the people. Then, they called them together, in order that they, too, might have a voice in plans for their freedom. They decided that the only way to rid themselves of the Lamanite yoke, would be to escape into the wilderness.

When the crowd had been dismissed, Gideon came and stood before the king, saying: "Oh king, you have listened to me before and always with profit and, now, I wish you would listen to me again, for I have a plan."

"Speak man, speak! What is your plan?" questioned the king, anxiously.

"My plan," said Gideon, excitedly, "is to gather our women and children, our flocks and herds, and all other things that we can carry with us and escape. We can go this very night, through the secret passage in the back wall of the city."

"Aren't you forgetting," said the king, "that an army of Lamanites is guarding every foot of the wall?"

"No," said Gideon. "But according to your custom, you send a tribute of wine to the guards. When they are drunken, they fall asleep, easily. Tonight, I will take the wine to them and when they are asleep, we can escape through the secret pass. We will go into the wilderness and travel around the land of Shilom."

The king listened to Gideon and liked what he heard. He sent out a proclamation, to all the people, telling them of Gideon's plan and commanding them to be ready, that very night. He sent the Lamanites more wine than ever before. The Lamanites were delighted with the extra tribute and drank deeply and freely of the wine. Soon, they fell asleep and the people of Limhi escaped, into the wilderness, with their flocks and herds and as many precious things as they could carry with them. They made their way around Shilom and headed toward the land of Zarahemla, with Ammon and his men, leading the way.

After many days of travel, they saw the beautiful land of Zarahemla and for the first time, since they left the land of Nephi, Limhi began to worry. He was, suddenly, afraid that King Mosiah would turn them out of his land. But when he told Ammon of his fears, Ammon laughed at him and said:

"Do not be afraid. You are Mosiah's people. He loves you just as dearly as he does any of us

You will see how glad he will be to welcome you home."

Ammon was right, for King Mosiah was overjoyed to have them home and they became his subjects. He was filled with joy to receive the records which were found in the land of many waters.

When the Lamanites discovered that the people of Limhi had escaped into the wilderness, they grew very angry and sent a great army to overtake them and bring them back. After they had followed them for two days, they could no longer see their tracks and then they became lost in the wilderness.

Limhi expected to see Alma and his followers, when he reached the land of Zarahemla; but no one had seen them. Where could they be? Perhaps, they had lost their way in the wilderness, or perhaps, after escaping from the wicked King Noah's army, they had been overtaken by the Lamanites and destroyed. This thought made Limhi sad and sick at heart, because he loved his people, very much. However, if Limhi had only known that Alma and his people were safe and were even then, entering the borders of Zarahemla, there would have been no need for sadness.

When Alma and the people of the Lord fled before King Noah's army, they went into the wilderness. On the morning of the eighth day, they climbed to the summit of a low mountain range and there, below them, lay a beautiful little valley. Alma thought it was the most pleasant spot he had ever seen. The valley floor was carpeted with rich green grass and in its center, lay a tiny lake, shimmering in the golden sunlight.

"This is the place," said Alma. "Here we will be safe for a while."

After so many days in the wilderness, the little valley looked like heaven to the travel-worn people of the Lord. When they reached the valley floor, they found the water crystal clear, ice cold and pure. They called their new found valley the land of Helam, and the city where they pitched their tents, they, also, called Helam. Immediately, they began to till the soil and build fine buildings. The Lord was pleased with their labors and made them prosper in the land. Now, the people loved Alma so much that they asked him to be their king.

"No," said Alma, "I will not be a king over you. We are all equal in the sight of the Lord. But I will teach you and lead you, in the ways of the Lord our God."

There was another reason why Alma felt he could not be king. He still remembered when he had served the wicked King Noah, as one of his evil priests. Alma had repented and had walked in the straight and narrow path. But, still, he wondered if God had fully forgiven him his past sins.

Alma spoke again, saying, "The Lord has freed you from the evil King Noah and I want you to value your freedom and trust no man to be a king over you."

Alma became their high priest and anyone who taught or served the people, in any way, received their right to do so through him. He taught them to love and help one another. Although God was pleased with the people of the Lord, still, he wanted to try their faith. Therefore, he let the Lamanites come upon them.

You will remember, how Limhi and his people, escaped from the land of Nephi and how the Lamanite army tried to find them, only to become lost in the wilderness. They wandered from place to place until, at last, they found the priests of Noah. Since the leader of the priests was called Amulon, they had named the land after him. The priests grew frightened, thinking that the Lamanites would kill them. Suddenly, Amulon thought of a way they might be saved, so he sent their wives to plead for them.

"Oh hear us, our fathers," said the priests' wives. "We are your lost daughters and we love you; but we are also the wives of the priests. We beg you to spare the lives of our husbands."

Now, when the Lamanites saw that it was really their lost daughters, and that they were happy with the priests, they did not destroy them. The priests joined the Lamanites and traveled with them, in the wilderness, in search of the land of Nephi. After they had wandered for many days, they came to Helam.

It happened that some of the people of Alma were in their fields, tilling the soil, when they saw the Lamanites approaching. They were overcome with fear, for the Lamanite army greatly outnumbered Alma's people. When they saw them coming, they took to their heels and ran as fast as they could, to the city of Helam. When they told Alma, he was unafraid. He asked them to pray to God, for His help, in their terrible hour of need. While the people prayed, Alma went forth alone, to meet the Lamanites. He soon discovered that they were lost and he promised to guide them back to the land of Nephi, if they would spare the lives of his people. However, after Alma had shown them the way, they didn't keep their promise. They set guards about the land of Helam. The Lamanite king made Amulon, the wicked priest, ruler over them. However, he was subject to the will of the king of the Lamanites.

The Lamanites began to be a mighty people. They ruled the land of Amulon, Helam, Shemlon, Shilom and Nephi. In all these lands, the Lamanite king made Amulon and the rest of the wicked priests teachers over the people. They taught the Lamanites the language of Nephi and how to keep their records. They taught them many useful things; but they forgot to teach them the most important thing of all—that God lives and expects us to keep His command-

ments. They were a friendly people to each other.
Soon, they began to grow rich and with their riches,
they became cunning and delighted in all manner of
wickedness.

"Mother, why does Amulon hate my father,
Alma?" asked Ruth, a young girl whose eyes were
too sad for her years.

"Alma and Amulon were once King Noah's
priests and Amulon remembers that your father
turned against him and tried to save the life of the
Prophet, Abinadi. Amulon is still a wicked man, my
child, and he will try, in every way, to make your
father and all of us suffer," explained her mother.

"Did you know," asked Ruth, "that Amulon has
commanded us to stop our prayers to God, or he will
put us to death?"

Alma's wife, a beautiful woman in spite of the
deep lines of care, sighed heavily and answered,
"Ruth, my dear, his command won't stop us from
praying in our hearts. God will hear us just as well
as though we spoke aloud. In fact, He has already
answered our prayers by making us strong enough
to carry our burdens without getting tired."

Just at that moment, Alma opened the door and
came to where Ruth and her mother sat talking.
There was a glow about his face that made his wife
and daughter look at him, carefully.

"Alma," said his wife, "you look very happy;
perhaps, I should say, more alive and glowing than

I have ever seen you. Tell us what has happened."

"The Lord has just spoken to me," said Alma, seating himself in front of them. "He has told me, that this very night, we are to gather our flocks, our grain and all we have and, on the morrow, He will lead us out of bondage. Come now, let us do as the Lord has commanded."

In the morning, the Lord caused a deep sleep to fall upon the Lamanites. Alma and all his people, together with their flocks and their possessions, went safely out of the land of Helam. After they had traveled twelve days, they came to the land of Zarahemla. Mosiah received them with joy.

CHAPTER 6

It was springtime, in the land of Zarahemla, and the air was heavy with the perfume of blossoming trees. Throughout all the land, there was rejoicing and thanksgiving over the coming of the people of Limhi and the people of Alma. They were gathered in two great groups. All the descendants of Zarahemla were called the people of Zarahemla and all the descendants of Nephi were called the people of Nephi. Now, the people of Zarahemla greatly outnumbered the people of Nephi; but the Lamanites outnumbered both of them, two to one.

King Mosiah made Alma the spiritual leader of the people and gave him the right to baptize them and establish churches in the land. Alma worked faithfully, baptizing all those who believed in Christ and establishing churches with priests and teachers over each church. There were seven churches, since one church could not serve them all.

Today, Alma was visiting his friend, Mosiah, at the palace. They were seated in the king's favorite spot, near a huge window, which overlooked the city. King Mosiah was watching his old friend with anxious eyes. Something was troubling him. He longed to help him; but he was at a loss to know what to do.

"Zarahemla is beautiful in springtime," said Alma, avoiding the subject that saddened him.

"Zarahemla is beautiful at all times of the year; but I think she outdoes herself in the springtime. This is a great people and a glorious land," said King Mosiah, with pride.

"Yes, yes," said Alma, absently.

"I'm sure you didn't come to discuss the springtime, or even this precious land of promise. Tell me old friend, what bothers you?" said Mosiah, in a voice warm with understanding.

Alma sighed heavily and said, "You know, as well as I do, of the wickedness of a number of our young people. They refuse baptism and even deny Christ. I came to you once, asking that you deal with them; but you put the responsibility on me. I prayed, earnestly, to God for His guidance. His voice came into my mind, telling me that all those who would repent and confess their sins, should be numbered among His people; but all those who would not repent of their sins, should be dropped from His church."

"Have you carried out God's command?" asked the king.

"Yes, indeed I have," said Alma, quickly. "A great many unbelievers have repented and confessed their sins and are now members of the church. However, the number of unbelievers grows larger, each day. It makes me very sad; but something else has happened that overshadows this. I need you to deal with it."

"I shall be glad to help you in any way I can," said King Mosiah, anxious to be of service to his unhappy friend.

"Thank you," said Alma. "A terrible thing has happened. The unbelievers have begun tormenting the people of the church. They steal from their flocks and herds and destroy their crops. There are five young men who ride together, at night, and commit all sorts of sins."

As Alma talked on, the king's anger grew until, at last, he brought his fist down, heavily, on the arm of his chair and shouted, "I'll deal with them. I won't have my people mistreating each other. Today, I will send a proclamation, warning them that they must stop their wickedness, or answer to me. You can be sure, my friend, I won't deal lightly with them."

"There is something I must tell you, although I dread speaking the words aloud," said Alma, greatly disturbed. "The five young men, who are the leaders in this wickedness, are your four sons and my son, Alma." Alma waited for the king to speak; but when he was too shocked to reply, Alma continued: "These sons of ours have silver tongues. They flatter the people until, in their pride, they are easily led into sin."

The king sat with bowed head, saying nothing and Alma sought for magic words to comfort him in his great disappointment. Now, Mosiah was a just man and he had thought, until now, that his sons were following in his footsteps.

A few days later, on a dark moonless night, five young men rode along the countryside, mounted on five spirited black horses, bent upon destruction. Their talk was loud and boastful. Young Alma was making light of those who believed in Christ, when suddenly, the earth began to tremble violently—so violently that they were thrown to the ground. They saw an angel, descending from heaven, in a cloud. He spoke to them in a voice of thunder. The five young men were so frightened they failed to hear his words; but he spoke again and this is what he said:

"Alma, arise and come here. Why do you do these evil things against the Church of God? The Lord has heard the prayers of His people and your father, Alma, has, also, prayed with great faith, asking God to give you a knowledge of the truth. For that reason, I have come to convince you of the power of God. Behold, my voice shakes the earth. You can see me and you know that I am sent from heaven. I say to you, go your way and do not destroy the church."

With these words, the angel disappeared. Alma and the four sons of King Mosiah, fell again to the earth, so great was their astonishment. They had seen the angel with their own eyes and heard his voice, which was like thunder. They had felt the earth shake beneath them and they knew that it had all come through the power of God. When Alma tried to arise, a strange thing happened. He found that he was too weak to move. He could not, even, raise his hands. He tried to tell the king's sons; but he could not talk. When they saw that he was helpless, they picked him up and carried him to his father. When they told Alma all that had happened, he rejoiced and gathered a great multitude together, that they might see what the Lord had done for his son.

"Will all the priests come forward?" asked Alma. "I should like you to fast and pray that the Lord will open the mouth of my son and let him speak again. And also, that his limbs might again be strong, in order that the people can see the goodness of God."

They prayed and fasted for two days and two nights. At the end of that time, young Alma arose and began to speak to the people, saying, "I have repented of my sins and the Lord has forgiven me. I am born again of the Spirit. I walked in darkness; but now, I have seen the marvelous light of God. My soul was in great torment; but now, I am without pain."

From this time forward, Alma, and the four sons of King Mosiah, began to teach the people. They traveled throughout all the land, telling the people what they had seen and teaching the Word of God. All five of them became instruments in the hands of God, bringing many to a knowledge of the truth.

At dusk, one day in late summer, Mosiah walked in his garden. It was his custom to come here, each day, during the twilight hours. Here, away from the rest of the world, he walked and talked with God. He had solved many a problem in this peaceful spot; but this evening, his heart was, especially, heavy. At last, weary with the burden of his thoughts, he sank down upon a garden bench and buried his face in his hands. For many days, his four sons had pled with him to let them go up to the land of Nephi, to teach the Lamanites the word of God. For the first time in his life, he had known fear. He knew, now, that he was afraid of loneliness—afraid that he would never see his sons again and most of all, that the Lamanites would destroy them. As the evening shadows closed in upon him, he slipped from the bench and knelt beside it.

"Oh, Lord God," he prayed, "should I let my sons go up to the land of Nephi, to teach Your word to our brethren, the Lamanites?"

As he continued to kneel beside the bench, the voice of the Lord came into his mind, saying, "Let them go, for many shall believe in their words and they shall return alive. I will deliver your sons out of the hands of the Lamanites." Mosiah arose, feeling more rested and happy than he had done for many days. He went to the palace and told his sons that their wish was granted. Immediately, they set out upon their journey.

Mosiah watched them go and with their going, he knew he had no son upon which to confer his kingdom or the records. Therefore, he took the brass plates, the plates of Nephi and all other records, together with the interpreters and conferred them upon young Alma. He commanded him to care for them and also to keep a record of his people, handing it down from one generation to another, just as had been done since Lehi left Jerusalem.

A few days after the king's sons had left the land of Zarahemla, Mosiah sent throughout all the land, among all the people, asking them to tell him whom they wanted to be their king.

The people answered, "We want Aaron, your son, to be our king and our ruler."

It was with a heavy heart that Mosiah told the people Aaron could not be their king, since he had left the kingdom. Neither could any of his other sons. He had much to say against having a king. In order that they would all hear what he had to say, he sent his written word among all the people. He told them he would be their king until his death, and at his passing, he thought it wise to appoint judges to judge the people according to their law, given them by God. The people were convinced. After much thought, they appointed young Alma to be the first chief judge. He was, also, the high priest of the church. He walked in the ways of the Lord, keeping His commandments and judging the people, fairly.

Throughout all the land, there was peace and happiness.

Alma's father passed away, at the age of eighty-two, having lived to fulfill the commandments of God. A few days later, King Mosiah died at the age of sixty-three, just 509 years from the time Lehi left Jerusalem. Thus ended the reign of the kings over the people of Nephi and thus ended the days of Alma who was the founder of their church.

CHAPTER 7

Alma, as head of the church and first chief judge of Zarahemla, was kept very busy. So busy, in fact, that there was seldom enough hours, in a day, to do all the things that needed his attention. He was a good man; kind and just. He loved his people dearly and watched over them with tender care. The people, on their part, returned his love and respect; but, nevertheless, he was on trial because he represented the new form of government. They sometimes wondered if they would be sorry they had given up their rule, by kings. They watched and waited for the first sign of success or failure. They didn't have long to wait; for a man, named Nehor, soon put him to the test.

One day, word came to Alma that there was a man, going up and down the land, telling the people that the priests and teachers of the church, should not belittle themselves by working. The people should support them. Furthermore, he taught that God made them all and no matter what they did, He would love and forgive them. Now, this was an easy belief to follow and many of the people, who were weak, found his ideas to their liking. This man was Nehor. Soon, he broke away from the church and started a new one, based on his teachings. He made the people support him with all sorts of riches and gay clothing.

For a long time, there was no word of Nehor. Alma had almost forgotten about him when, suddenly, the news was brought to him that Nehor had killed a man. The whole land of Zarahemla was stirred by the news. The law said a life for a life. If Alma let the sin go unpunished, it would lead to other crimes and many of them would be slaves again. They remembered Mosiah's reign and the freedom they enjoyed under his protecting care.

Alma learned that the man, who had been killed, was his good friend, Gideon—the same Gideon, who had led Limhi and his people out of bondage. He learned, too, that Gideon had come to the defense of the church of God and had told Nehor he was leading the people away from the true church. Nehor became angry and struck Gideon several blows. Gideon was an old man and being old and weak, he died. Alma commanded that Nehor be brought before him, that he might be judged according to the law.

Alma was seated by a long table, busily recording the history of his people, when the door opened and they brought Nehor before him. He looked up and for a moment, he was so surprised that he sat speechless, observing the man before him. Nehor was a great giant of a man. His eyes were as cold as steel and just as hard. His huge mouth was curled into an evil smile. At last, Alma's gaze rested on Nehor's hands. Never, in all his life, had he seen such huge hands and now, they were restlessly opening and shutting as though they would like to be about Alma's neck. The guards, who brought him in, had fallen back and were now huddled together for protection. There was no fear in Alma's eyes; only righteous anger. The guards marveled at his courage and when he spoke, his voice was clear and steady:

"Nehor, you have taken a man's life. What have you to say for yourself?"

"I was forced to defend myself against an old man and his crazy ideas," said Nehor, boldly.

"It must have taken all the courage you had to defend yourself against a weak old man." Alma spoke with disgust.

Suddenly, Nehor threw back his head and laughed loudly, thinking it a good joke. And then, just as suddenly, his mood changed to black fury. He beat upon his chest and shouted, "Nehor is not afraid of any man; not even you, Chief Judge."

He stepped close to Alma and thrust his evil face forward. Alma met his cruel eyes, without fear, while the guards trembled violently at a safe distance.

"Are you guilty of killing Gideon?" asked Alma, in a voice that had a strange effect upon Nehor for, at that instant, the great giant, suddenly, became a weakling. He began begging for mercy. Alma knew that it was through the power of the Lord that Nehor was given over into his hands.

"You have shed the blood of a good man. Yes, a man who has done much good among this people. The law says, a life for a life. Therefore, I condemn you to die."

They carried him to the top of the hill, Manti, and there, before he died, he confessed that what he taught the people was not the word of God. In spite of his death, it did not put an end to sin. The vain, proud people continued to break away from the church and they did many cruel things to the children of God.

The fifth year, of the rule of the judges, was long to be remembered, because it was a year of great bitterness and heartbreak. When the people of the church could no longer stand the abuse of the unbelievers, they went to war against them. The unbelievers were driven out of Zarahemla; but they were not defeated for behold, they joined with the Lamanites and came back into the land of Zarahemla. A terrible war was fought, in which thousands were killed.

The first year, following the war, was a time of suffering both in mind and body, for the people of Zarahemla. There was scarcely a family, in all the land, who hadn't lost a loved one or more. Their fields, of grain, had been beaten into the earth by the armies. Their flocks and herds were almost destroyed. The cries, of hungry children, were heard on every hand. They became a humble people and turned to God in their hour of need and He heard their prayers and blessed them.

By the eighth year, of the reign of the judges, they had become a prosperous people. Many of them had become worldly; thinking only of their riches. Alma watched them, with a heavy heart, and wondered how they could forget their suffering and their need for God, so quickly. At last, desperate in his desire to help them before the Lord grew angry, he gave up his position as chief judge, in order to spend all his time as high priest of the church. He, therefore, appointed a faithful elder, as chief judge, to rule in his stead. This man's name was Nephihah.

Alma spent all his time, teaching the people and bringing them to the remembrance of the goodness and mercy of God. He traveled throughout all the land of Zarahemla and, finally his labors began to bear fruit—the people turned to God and began to keep His commandments, once more. Then Alma went over into the valley of Gideon and successfully taught the people God's word. Hundreds of them were baptized and rejoiced in being members of the true church. From the land of Gideon, he went to Melek and the people blessed him for bringing the gospel to them.

When Alma left Melek, he did so with a light heart and a sense of deep satisfaction. It was a pleasant morning, in early fall, and Alma was happier than he had ever been. He knew it was because he was spending his time, bringing the people the word of God. He breathed deeply of the fresh, pure air as he turned his footsteps north, to the city of Ammonihah. Part, of the journey, led through a forest. Through the trees, he caught sight of many wild animals; but he was unafraid, for he knew he walked with God. He traveled for three days and then, at last, he saw the beautiful city of Ammonihah. Even, before he entered the city, he felt a strange, unfriendly spirit. It was so strong that he hesitated, wondering if he should turn back. However, he soon overcame his doubts and entered the city and began, at once, to preach to the people. Little did he know that Satan had already taken hold of the hearts of the people. Because of this fact, they would not listen to his words. At last the people said:

"We know you are Alma, the high priest of the church; but we do not believe in the things you teach, therefore, you have no power over us. We know, too, that you are no longer chief judge, over this people and, for this reason, we demand that you leave our city."

The people said many evil things to Alma. They spit upon him and cast him out. Sick at heart, he turned his footsteps toward the city, called Aaron. As he walked along, he was weighed down with sorrow because of the wickedness of the people of Ammonihah. Suddenly, an angel appeared to him. It was the same angel he had seen, as a young man, when he and Mosiah's sons had ridden out to destroy the property of the people of the church. This time, however, he was not afraid; but his heart was filled with joy. He knew the angel was there to help him.

The angel spoke, saying, "You are blessed. Lift up your head and rejoice. You have great cause to rejoice, for you have been faithful, in keeping the commandments of God, from the time you received my first message. I am sent, now, to command you to return to the city of Ammonihah and preach again to the people. Tell them that if they do not repent, the Lord will destroy them."

As soon as Alma received the message, he hurried back to the city. But this time, he entered by another way. He was very hungry and he remembered that he had had nothing to eat for many days.

Alma said to a man, standing near the entrance, "Will you give a humble servant of God something to eat?"

"Good evening. I have been waiting for you," said the man, quietly.

"Waiting to see me?" asked Alma, astonished. "But you are a stranger. How could you possibly know me?"

"You are Alma, a holy prophet of God," answered the man, smiling at Alma's confusion.

"That is my name; but how do you know me? Who are you?" asked Alma, tired of the riddle.

"My name is Amulek and I am a Nephite. Early

today, an angel appeared to me and told me to wait here for you. Come with me, to my home. I will feed you. Your presence will bring a rich blessing to my house."

Alma followed Amulek to his home, still astonished by all that had happened. When he had eaten Amulek's bread, he thanked God for His wonderful power and he asked that Amulek's house be blessed. Now, Alma stayed with Amulek for many days, until at last, the Word of God came to him, saying:

"Go forth and preach My word to this people. Take Amulek with you and have him testify of the things he has seen. Call upon the people to repent. Tell them if they don't repent, I shall be very angry with them—so angry, in fact, that I will destroy them."

They went forth and began to preach to the people of Ammonihah. Alma reminded them of the promise God made to Lehi when he reached the promised land. He said, that if this people would keep His commandments and walk in the straight and narrow path, they would prosper in the land. But if they would not keep His commandments, He would destroy them. Alma pointed out how God had kept His promise. He reminded them, also, of the curse that fell upon the Lamanites, because of the wickedness of Laman, Lemuel and the sons of Ishmael.

The words of Alma and Amulek fell upon deaf ears and hardened hearts. The more they preached,

to the people of Ammonihah, the more wicked they
became. With their wickedness, came a deep hatred
for these holy men of God. They tried to slay them;
but they could not, for they were filled with the spirit
of the Holy Ghost. Then they took them and bound
them fast and threw them into prison. The judges,
of the land, came to the prison each day, to abuse
Alma and Amulek. Their suffering was so great that
Alma called upon God to free them from the hands
of their enemies. Lo and behold God sent His mighty
power and they stood up and the cords that bound
them, fell away as if they were nothing. The earth
trembled so violently that the walls of the prison
began to crack and crumble. At last, the whole prison
fell to the earth, leaving Alma and Amulek safe and
free. Now, all the others, who were in the prison,
lost their lives. The Lord had granted this power
unto Alma and Amulek, according to their faith,
which was in Christ.

When the people, in the city of Ammonihah,
heard the great noise and felt the trembling earth,
they ran forth, in a great multitude, to the prison.
They could scarcely believe their eyes when they saw
their strong prison in ruins. Every living creature
was dead except Alma and Amulek. Suddenly, they
were struck with fear and turned and fled before the
two holy men of God.

CHAPTER 8

Alma and Amulek turned their backs on the city of Ammonihah, and left the wicked people to their own devices. They traveled, slowly, back to the land of Zarahemla.

"I am without a home," said Amulek.

"My home shall be your home," said Alma, placing a friendly hand upon his companion's shoulder.

In the eleventh year of the reign of the judges, after many years of peace, a cry of war was heard throughout the land. The armies of the Lamanites came into the city of Ammonihah and began to slay the people and destroy the city. Before the Nephites could raise an army large enough to drive them out, they had destroyed most of the people and had taken the rest captive. There was not one living soul left in the entire city. And thus, the word of the Lord was fulfilled. For years to come, it was a place of ruin and complete desolation.

Early in the fifteenth year of the reign of the judges, there was peace and plenty throughout all the lands of the Nephites. Much of the credit was due to Alma and his good friend Amulek. They spent all their time going among the people, teaching them in the ways of the Lord and stirring them to remember God's loving mercy to the faithful and His terrible anger against those who sinned. Their labors were well rewarded, for most of the people were humble and faithful to God and to each other.

Today, Alma was following the trail that led away from Gideon and southward, toward the land of Manti. It was high noon and the day was hot and still. Where the sun touched his hands and face, it felt scorching hot. He was hungry; but there was no sign of shade and he disliked the thought of eating his bread and cheese in the burning heat of the sun. He knew that, at the bottom of the slope, the path turned and led into meadow country. Here, the trail was bordered on either side by two rows of willow trees, their lacy branches interlocking with each other, making a long tunnel of green. The very thought of this cool, inviting spot brought a smile to his lips. The smile disappeared when he remembered the stories he had heard, concerning the mishaps, that had befallen certain travelers. On several occasions, bands of Lamanites had surprised lonely travelers, robbing and beating them. In spite of the stories, he had heard, he decided he must get out of the burning rays of the sun, at any cost. As he made the turn, he came into full view of the little meadow valley, with its graceful willow trees. It was like a fairyland, with a thin veil of mist, hanging over it, making it all seem a bit unreal. Here and there, could be seen pools of sparkling, clear water. It was a paradise for birds, and all living creatures, who loved God's great out-of-doors.

Alma stopped to rest and have time to look for any signs of Lamanites, knowing they could easily hide among the shadowy willows. As soon as he reached the willow lane, its cool freshness seemed to give him new strength. He chose a spot under a huge willow tree and sat down upon the ground to eat his meal. Suddenly, he was alert to a sound among the trees. He sat silent; almost afraid to breathe. When the sound came again, he knew that whatever it was, it was walking toward him. In fact, it was very near. The fingers, of his right hand, found the handle of his hunting knife and closed upon it. Suddenly, the head of a donkey poked through the drooping branches of the willow tree.

When the donkey saw Alma, he was so surprised that he sat down upon his back legs and cried, "Hee-haw! Hee-haw! Hee-haw!"

"Don't be a foolish old fellow, I'm not going to harm you," said Alma, laughing at the comical donkey.

At that moment, he noticed a short broken rope around the donkey's neck. Furthermore, he noticed a pack on its back. He had been so occupied with the donkey, he failed to hear the voices of men approaching. As soon as he heard them, he went to the edge of the trail and looked southward and there, coming toward him, were four men. Immediately, he returned to the donkey and took hold of his rope.

"Come little donkey, I need you to make friends

for me," Alma said, and he led the donkey to the path.

Instantly, the men caught sight of him and to his great surprise, one of them called his name. He saw, then, that it was the four sons of King Mosiah. Ammon, the eldest, was the first to reach him. They were all overjoyed to see each other again. They had shared a wonderful experience together. These were the five men to whom the angel appeared, fourteen years before, and caused them to forsake their sins and walk in the ways of the Lord.

"Is this your donkey?" asked Alma.

"Yes, it is," they answered. "He broke away from the pack train. But, come, we have better things to talk about than the runaway donkey."

"Where are you going?" asked Alma.

"We are returning to Zarahemla. It won't seem the same without our father or mother. Come, sit down and tell us all about the things that have happened, since we have been among the Lamanites."

Alma was only too glad to give them a full account of the happenings of their people, in and about the land of Zarahemla. When he finished, he asked that they tell him of their labors, among the Lamanites.

Alma rejoiced at seeing his friends again. But his joy knew no bounds, when he learned that they had walked in the ways of the Lord since the angel appeared to them. They had prayed and fasted often until, at last, through their great faith, God had given them the power of prophecy. They were men of great understanding and through their constant study of the records, they had come to know the word of God. And when they taught His word, it was with authority from on high. For fourteen years they had labored among the Lamanites, and because of their good example and their knowledge of the truth, they had had great success in converting them to the gospel. The sons of Mosiah had met with many hardships. Often, their lives were in danger and they had suffered, both in mind and body. They had been hungry, thirsty, tired and discouraged. But, through their prayers and God's watchful eye, they had overcome great obstacles.

CHAPTER 9

Alma and the sons of Mosiah talked all through the day and far into the night. As if by special arrangement, just as twilight was fading into night, a full moon rose in a cloudless sky, blessing them with its white, silvery light. Now, as the others lay sleeping, Alma lay wide awake. He was thinking of all they had told him about their experiences with the Lamanites, beginning fourteen years earlier. Ammon had done most of the talking.

When the sons of Mosiah and those who went with them, had reached the Lamanite borders, they had prayed and fasted. They asked God that a portion of His Holy Spirit be with them, so that they might impart the truth to the Lamanites. They asked Him, also, for courage in their labors. Now, it required a great deal of courage, because the Lamanites were a wild and hard-hearted people. They hated the Nephites with a fierce and terrible hatred. But, with faith in God, the sons of Mosiah parted company, each going in a different direction. They prayed that they would meet again, when their labors were completed.

Ammon went to the land of Ishmael. This land was named after the sons of Ishmael, who joined with Laman and Lemuel and they became known as the Lamanites. Just as Ammon entered their land, he was set upon by several men. They bound him and took him to their king. This was the practice they always followed when they captured a Nephite. It was left to the pleasure of the king to decide the fate of the victim.

Lamoni was king over the land of Ishmael and when he saw Ammon, he looked at him, suspiciously, and asked, "What are you doing in my land? Do you wish to live here, among my people?"

Ammon answered him, saying, "Yes, I should like to live here among your people, perhaps, until I die."

The words of Ammon pleased King Lamoni so much, he ordered that the ropes, that bound him, be loosened.

"I will give you one of my daughters to be your wife," said King Lamoni, smiling at the surprised look on Ammon's face.

"I do not wish so great an honor. I shall be very happy to be your servant," said Ammon, humbly.

King Lamoni, like the rest of his people, had been taught, from early childhood, to hate and distrust the Nephites; but, in spite of himself, he found it pleasant to talk with Ammon. Yes, he even liked him. However, he meant to test him, so he said, "Take Ammon to my servants who tend my flocks. I want him to help them."

Ammon was delighted. He liked working outside. He had often tended his father's flocks. He

knew, too, that, in this way, he would have an oppor-
tunity to teach the word of God. Little did he know,
that in a very short time, he would find himself in
real danger. He prayed, silently, for God to provide
a way to touch their hearts, so that they would listen
to the truths he wanted to teach them.

Water, for the flocks and herds, was scarce in
the land of Ishmael. For this reason, more than one
man's animals had to use the same watering place.
On the morning of the third day, Ammon and the
other servants drove the king's flocks to the place
called Sebus. It was a pleasant morning and as
Ammon watched the thirsty animals drink the clear,
cool water, he felt happier than he had for a long
time. He was deep within his own thoughts, when
he realized that something was happening to the
animals. Looking up, he saw a number of strange
Lamanites scattering the flocks. This was the custom of certain bands of Lamanites. They would wait
at the watering place and scatter the animals, in all
directions, in the hope that they could drive off part
of them for themselves.

The king's servants began to cry out, in fear,
saying, "The king will surely slay us as he has done
with our brethren, who lost the flocks, in the same
manner."

Ammon saw, at once, that the servants were too
frightened to even try to get the animals back. Therefore, with a prayer in his heart, he said, with firm

conviction, "Do not be afraid, for we can easily get the flocks back again, if we work fast."

Ammon's words so encouraged them, that they ran around the flocks and brought them back to the water. But, the wicked men were still there and came forth to scatter them again.

"Encircle the animals," said Ammon, "and see that they do not run away, while I go forward and talk with these men."

King Lamoni's servants hurried to do as Ammon commanded. There was something about his voice that made them feel that they could trust him. When he walked toward the men, who stood on the banks of Sebus, the king's servants watched him with fear and trembling. When Ammon was within speaking distance, he called out to the wicked Lamanites:

"Stand aside and let us water our flocks! If you do not, you will be sorry, for some of you may be destroyed."

The men roared with laughter. They were great in number and they thought that any time they wished, one of them could go forth and kill Ammon. But there was something they did not know—Mosiah had been promised, by the Lord, that his sons would be delivered out of their hands. Nor did they know the great power of the Lord when one has faith, like Ammon.

When Ammon saw that they did not mean to let them come near the water, he took his sling and began casting stones at them. Six of their number were struck and fell to the ground, while not one single stone hit Ammon. When the wicked Lamanites saw what was happening, they picked up huge clubs and came forward to kill Ammon. But when they raised their clubs, Ammon smote them with his sword and they were unable to harm him. They were so astonished, at his great power, that they turned and ran away. Then he returned to the king's servants and, together, they watered the flocks and drove them home to the king's pastures.

The servants hurried to the king to tell him what had happened. He was so astonished, that he asked them whether Ammon was really a man or the Great Spirit.

"We don't know; but we do know that he cannot be killed by the king's enemies."

When Ammon came to the king, he found him in great distress. He was afraid to speak. But Ammon, knowing what was in the king's mind, told him not to be afraid.

"How did you know my thoughts? Who are you? Are you the Great Spirit who knows all things?" asked the bewildered king.

"I am not," answered Ammon.

"If you will tell me how you get your great power, I will grant you anything you ask for," said the king, with great excitement.

Now Ammon, being a wise man and entirely

unselfish, said, "Will you listen to my words, if I tell you how I got this great power?"

"Yes," answered the king. "I will believe anything you tell me." And thus, he placed himself in Ammon's hands.

"Do you believe there is a God?" asked Ammon.

"I don't know what that means."

"Do you believe there is a Great Spirit?"

"Yes," said Lamoni.

"This is God," said Ammon. "Do you believe this Great Spirit, who is God, made all things in heaven and earth?"

"Yes, I believe that He created all things on earth; but I do not know about heaven."

"Heaven is a place where God and all His Holy Angels dwell."

The king sat silent, trying to understand the marvelous things he had heard. At last, when he spoke, his voice was full of faith: "I believe all that you have told me. Are you sent from God?"

Ammon said to him, "I am a man and man was created in the image of God. I am called, by Him, to teach your people to know what is just and true."

Then Ammon told him all about the creation of the world, down to the time that Lehi left Jerusalem and of how Laman and Lemuel and the sons of Ishmael had rebelled.

The king believed all that he heard and he began

to cry to the Lord, saying, "Oh Lord, have mercy on my people. Bless us, as you have the Nephites."

As soon as the king had spoken these words, he fell to the earth as if he were dead. The servants carried him to his wife and laid him upon his bed. He lay, as if he were dead, for two days and two nights. His wife, his sons and his daughters wept aloud, because of their great loss.

On the second day, the servants said to each other, "Our king is dead and we must bury him. Let us go and tell the queen."

"No," said the queen, when they told her, "The king is not dead."

The servants were surprised to hear the queen's words and they looked at each other, as much as to say, "Our queen is mad. Her great grief has destroyed her reason."

Now, the queen knew their thoughts, so she commanded, "Go, bring Ammon, the Nephite, to me. You men, who tend the flocks, have said he is a true prophet of the Great Spirit. He will know what to do."

When Ammon came, he was overjoyed to learn what great faith the queen had.

"The king is alive. At this time tomorrow, he will arise from his bed," said Ammon.

Now, Ammon knew that the Lord had used this means to take away the veil of darkness, from the mind of the king and to fill his being with God's holy light. The queen sat by her husband until the next day. Then, just as Ammon had said, the king arose from his bed.

"You are blessed, my queen. I have seen a wonderful vision. I saw the Redeemer and I know that He will come, to earth, and save mankind."

Then, he prayed until he was overcome and fell to earth again. In a few minutes, the queen, Ammon and all the king's servants fell to the earth. They lay as though they were dead. There was one who did not fall. Her name was Abish. For many years, she had known about the ways of the Lord. Her father had had a remarkable vision. She thought, if all the people could see the king and queen and all the others lying upon the ground, they would believe in the power and goodness of the Lord. Therefore, she ran from house to house, until a great multitude had gathered about those lying upon the ground. They began to quarrel with each other. Some said that great evil had befallen the king and his household, because he let the Nephite stay. Others said that the Nephite had brought them the Lord's holy light. In the multitude, were some of the men who had scattered the king's flocks and, seeing Ammon lying on the ground, one of them came forward and raised his sword to kill him. Suddenly, he fell dead. This so frightened the crowd, that no one dared come near those who lay upon the ground, except Abish. She ran to the queen and touched her hand. To their surprise, the queen arose, and began praising the Lord. She took Lamoni by the hand and he and all the servants arose.

From that day forth, their hearts had been changed. They had no further desire to do evil. A great many of the people became baptized and a church was established in the land of Ishmael. The Lord began to pour out His spirit upon them, because of their repentance.

CHAPTER 10

A few days later, on a rain swept morning, King Lamoni and Ammon were rolling along in a chariot, drawn by two fine, white horses. The rain had stopped and the clouds began to lift, letting the sun stream through, touching the tiny raindrops, on the leaves, and changing them into brilliantly colored jewels. Ammon breathed deeply of the cool, fresh air and thought that the rich, green fields and woods were the most beautiful sight he had ever seen. In spite of the rough roads, the ride gave him great pleasure.

"You are a skillful driver," said Ammon. "I notice you miss most of the ruts."

"Oh," said King Lamoni, "it's easier than you think. See how the rain has marked each rut clearly. Something has been puzzling me, Ammon."

"Something about me?" asked Ammon.

"Yes," answered Lamoni. "When I asked you to come, with me, to the land of Nephi that you might meet my father, who is king over all the land of the Lamanites, you objected. You said you must go to the land of Middoni, because your brother Aaron and two of his friends were in prison there. Tell me, how did you know this?"

"God told me," said Ammon, simply.

Lamoni turned and looked at Ammon, in surprise, at the matter-of-fact way in which his friend spoke of God—just as though He were one of their companions. And, indeed, He was. A portion of His spirit was with Ammon wherever he went.

Suddenly, they heard the rumble of another chariot coming toward them. Looking up, Ammon saw two beautiful, cream-colored horses drawing a chariot, trimmed in gold and precious stones. The rays of the sun made it glitter so brightly that he raised his hand to protect his eyes.

"It is my father," said Lamoni, as the chariot came to a stop beside them.

"Well, at last, I see you," roared the old king. "What kept you away from my feast?"

Patiently and with great feeling, Lamoni told his father all about how Ammon had converted him to the faith. For this reason, he had not been able to come to his father's palace. When his father heard his son's words, a terrible anger seized him.

"Where are you going with this Nephite, son of a liar?" questioned the old king.

"To Middoni, Father," answered Lamoni, quietly.

"And why do you go to Middoni?" he asked, sharply.

"To free Aaron and his two friends from prison."

"I've never heard of them before. Tell me who

they are and why they should concern you," demanded the king in a great, thundering voice.

"This is Ammon, Father, and it is his brother and his friends, who have been cast into prison. I go to plead, with the king of Middoni, in their behalf," said Lamoni, watching his father, carefully. The old man was not only his father but his king as well. He ruled his kingdoms with an iron hand and many a king had been destroyed by him.

When the king heard his son's words, color flooded his face. He grew so red that Ammon expected to see him explode into a thousand pieces. For a few seconds, he was unable to speak and when he did, his words were fierce with anger.

"You go to free the Nephites, children of liars? How dare you? They robbed our fathers and now, their children have come among us to deceive us, that they may again rob us of our property. I command you, as your king, to slay Ammon with your sword. Furthermore, I command you to stay away from Middoni. Turn around and go back, with me, to Ishmael."

Lamoni had always been more than a little afraid of his father; especially, when he was angry. But now, to his great surprise, he felt calm and unafraid.

"I will not slay Ammon," answered Lamoni. "Neither will I return to the land of Ishmael. I am going to Middoni to set the prisoners free. I know that they are just men and holy prophets of the true God."

When his father heard this, he drew his sword and raised it, as if to kill his son. Suddenly, Ammon came forward and said to him: "You must not kill your son. Nevertheless, it would be better that he died than you. He has repented of his sins; but if you should go in your anger, your soul could not be saved. If you slay your son, you will shed innocent blood."

While Ammon was speaking, the old king drew his sword and came, dangerously, near where Ammon was standing.

"I know," said the king, fiercely, "that if I kill my son, I will shed innocent blood. It is you who will destroy him."

In a wild rage, the king rushed toward Ammon, striking him, again and again, with his sword. But Ammon withstood all the blows; in fact, he didn't seem to mind them at all. At last, Ammon raised his sword and struck the arm of the king, making it useless. When the king realized what had happened —that he was now at the mercy of the Nephite, he began to plead for his life.

"Spare my life," he moaned, "and you shall have whatever you want, even if it be half my kingdom."

"If I spare your life, you must let Aaron and his friends go free. Furthermore, you must allow your son, Lamoni, to keep his kingdom and have a free hand in ruling it. Now, oh king, if you will grant these things, I will spare your life."

The king was astonished at Ammon's words. He fully expected him to demand riches and power. But Ammon had asked for neither. In fact, he hadn't asked for a thing for himself. This was a strange man, thought the king. In that moment, he knew how great was the love of the Nephite for his son, Lamoni. It warmed his heart and he forgot his hatred for the Nephites.

"Yes, yes," cried the old king. "I will grant all you have asked for and more. Come with me, to the land of Nephi, and dwell among us."

"Thank you," said Ammon, "but I go to Middoni, first, to free my brother from prison and then I shall return to Ishmael, to finish my mission there."

Lamoni's father made Ammon promise to come to the land of Nephi later, then the three of them parted, good friends.

The king of Middoni was happy to see King Lamoni . He gladly granted their request to set Aaron and his friends free. In a short time, the prisoners were brought to them. Ammon scarcely knew his brother; he was so thin and pale. All three of them were naked and where the ropes had bound them, their skin was raw and bleeding. Ammon felt sick at the thought of how they must have suffered. When Aaron and his friends had been clothed and fed, the two brothers sat down to have a long visit.

When they had finished, they said goodbye and departed in opposite directions.

Ammon returned, with Lamoni, to the land of Ishmael and spent all his time, going among the Lamanites, teaching them the word of God. Hundreds of them were converted and joined the church. King Lamoni sent his messengers throughout all his kingdom, telling the people that they were free to worship according to their desires.

After Aaron left Middoni, he was led by the Spirit, to the land of Nephi—yes, even to the king, ruler over all the lands, except Ishmael.

"Oh, King," said Aaron, "I am the brother of Ammon. If you will spare our lives, we will be your servants."

With these words, Aaron and his friends fell upon their knees before the old king.

"Arise," said the king. "Your lives are spared and all I ask in return, is that you teach me about the ways of the Lord."

It came to pass that the king, the queen and all their servants, became converted to the teachings of Aaron. The old king sent out a proclamation to all the Lamanites in his kingdom. He told them that Aaron and his three brothers, were to be free to teach the people, from house to house and in their churches. Furthermore, the people, themselves, were to be free to worship as they pleased. After this proclamation, thousands were converted to the Gospel of Jesus

Christ. They wanted to be given a name that would distinguish them from the non-believers of the Lamanites. From that day forth, they were known as the Anti-Nephi-Lehies.

One day, when the four sons of Mosiah chanced to meet, Ammon said to them: "We have met with great success in all our missionary labors. We have entered into their houses and taught them. We have taught them in the streets and upon their hills and in their temples. We have been cast out, mocked, spit upon, stoned and cast into prison. But, through the power and wisdom of God, we have always been delivered. We can, now, see the fruits of our labors. They are many and we can see their sincerity because of their love toward one another and toward us. There never has been such great love in all the land—not even among the Nephites. We have great reason to rejoice."

CHAPTER 11

The converted Lamanites, known as the Anti-Nephi-Lehies, were in grave danger. When they became members of the true church of God, they had buried their weapons of war and vowed never to take them up again, even though it be in defense of their own lives. Now, the wicked Lamanites knew this and they took advantage of it by stealing from their flocks and herds and their storehouses. They killed many of them, for no reason at all. When Ammon and his three brothers, saw this work of destruction, they were very sad for they loved them dearly, and they, in turn, loved the four brothers. The Lamanites treated them as though they were angels of God, sent to save their souls.

"Oh King, let us gather these people of the Lord and go down to the land of Zarahemla. There we will be with the Nephites, out of the hands of our enemies," said Ammon.

But the king said, "The Nephites will destroy us, because of our past sins against them."

Then Ammon said, "I will ask the Lord and if he tells us to go to Zarahemla, will you go?"

"Yes," said the king, "if the Lord tells us to go, then you can be sure we will go. We will offer ourselves as their slaves, until we have paid them back for our many sins against them."

"No," said Ammon, "that is not the way of the Nephites. Many years ago my father, Mosiah, established a law, forbidding slavery. Therefore, let us go down and rely upon their mercy."

But the king said to Ammon, "Go and ask the Lord and if He says go we will obey Him. Otherwise, we will perish in our land."

The Lord answered Ammon, saying, "Get this people out of this land, so that they will not be destroyed! Satan has a great hold on the hearts of the Lamanites. Blessed are the Anti-Nephi-Lehies, for I will preserve them."

They began, at once, to gather all the people of the Lord, all their flocks and herds and went into the wilderness, which divided the land of Nephi from the land of Zarahemla.

"My brothers and I," said Ammon, "will go to Zarahemla while you remain here, until we return. We will prepare the hearts of the Nephites, so that they will receive you into their land."

The four sons of King Mosiah set out, immediately, for the land of Zarahemla. It was on this very journey that they met Alma. They had talked for hours and they were overjoyed at meeting their friend. Early next morning, Alma awakened Ammon and his brothers.

"It is sunrise," said Alma. "It is time for us to begin our journey to Zarahemla."

"Do you mean you are going with us to Zarahemla?" asked Ammon, smiling his pleasure.

"Yes," answered Alma, "I thought, perhaps, I could help you, since I am high priest; but if you would rather go alone, I will understand."

Now, Ammon and his brothers were delighted at the prospect of having Alma with them. They had wanted to ask him to join them; but they had hesitated, since they knew he was doing missionary work among the Nephites. When they reached Zarahemla, they went, at once, to Alma's house.

"I would like you to share my home with me," said Alma.

The brothers were grateful for the invitation, since their father and mother had both passed away.

"First, we must see the chief judge of the land," said Ammon.

The chief judge was deeply touched by the story of the conversion of the Lamanites, known as the Anti-Nephi-Lehies. When he learned that they needed protection from their enemies, because they would not take up arms to protect themselves, he was anxious to help them. He sent a proclamation throughout all the land of the Nephites, asking the people what they wished to do, to help their brethren.

"We will watch over them," said the people, "and protect them from their enemies. They can have the land of Jershon, as the land of their inheritance. We will give them protection by placing our army between them and the wicked Lamanites."

Now, Jershon was a beautiful land, in the east, by the sea. It joined the land Bountiful. Alma and Ammon returned to the Anti-Nephi-Lehies, where they waited in the wilderness. They were grateful to learn of the generosity of the people of Zarahemla. When they entered Jershon, they blessed the land and began, at once, to build their homes. They were honest and upright, in every way, and they were firm in the faith of Christ, to the very end. The Nephites learned to love them and they became a highly favored people.

One afternoon, during the seventeenth year of the reign of the judges, Alma and his good wife, sat in their comfortable living room. Alma had been reading; but now, he pushed the record from him and leaned back in the chair and closed his eyes. In a few minutes, he sat up and watched his wife, mending his tunic. Because of his great love for her, he thought her beautiful. She wasn't beautiful at all; but rather plain. She felt his eyes upon her and looking up, she smiled at him. There was magic in her smile. It changed her plain features into sweet, loveliness and made her dark eyes sparkle.

"You're not forgetting your appointment with the chief judge, are you?" she asked.

"No," replied Alma.

"You look troubled. Is this meeting worrying you?" asked his wife.

"Yes," said Alma. "He is an evil man."

"Of whom do you speak?" she questioned.
"Korihor!"

"Korihor," she said. "I don't believe I have heard of him."

"He is a wicked man. He denies the prophets of our God and he goes so far as to deny the coming of Christ. He says there is no God and that those of us, who claim there is, only do so in order that we can live from the labors of the people."

An angry flush crept into the cheeks of Alma's wife. No one knew better than she, that he had never allowed anyone to support him; even when he spent most of his time going among the people, teaching them the ways of God. There had been times, when he and his family had gone hungry to help others. When Alma saw her anger, he soothed her by putting his arm, tenderly, about her shoulders.

"Well, at last, this man has gotten himself arrested and he is to be judged this very afternoon. Now, I must go. The chief judge wants me to hear what Korihor has to say for himself."

Alma reached the bar of justice before the prisoner. At last, when they brought him in, he was very angry. Alma studied his face and found it evil and cowardly.

Korihor said, "I deny that there is a Christ or that there ever will be one; but if you will show me a sign, I might believe. Surely, your God is powerful enough to give me a sign."

"You need no sign," said Alma, "for all about you, bears testimony of God. How dare you tempt Him by asking for a sign? Think well, before you make Him angry. Now, do you still want a sign?"

The corners of Korihor's mouth curled into an evil smile, as he said, "Yes, I shall deny all these things, unless you show me a sign." ·

"I am very sorry to learn how hard hearted you are and since you deny the spirit, which teaches all of us what the real truth is, you may lose your soul. But, perhaps, it is better that one man lose his soul, than the many that you are leading astray, by your lying. Now, if you dare deny again, God will strike you dumb. You will never open your mouth again, to destroy this people." Alma's voice was low and pleading. He was deeply grieved, for the terrible thing Korihor was demanding.

But Korihor threw back his head and laughed. "I do not believe there is a God," he said. "And, furthermore, you do not know there is one either. Show me a sign, if you can."

"Very well," said Alma. "You shall be struck dumb and I say this in the name of God. From this day forward, you shall not speak again."

When Alma had said this, Korihor found that he was dumb. He tried and tried to speak; but no words would come. Then he pulled on his tongue; but that did not help.

The chief judge said to him: "Are you convinced now, of God's power?"

Korihor wrote these words, in answer: "I know that I am dumb. I cannot speak. I know that no one, but God, could have such power. Behold, I have been deceived by the devil, for he appeared to me, in the form of an angel. I have taught his words. Alma, ask God to forgive me that I may have this curse taken away."

Alma said, "If this curse was taken away, you would again lead the people astray. Therefore, it shall remain until the Lord wills it otherwise."

From that day forward, everyone knew of Korihor and the terrible curse that had been placed upon him. All those who heard his words, were frightened and began to repent. They feared that the Lord would strike them dumb, also. Now, Korihor went from house to house, begging for his food. One day, while he begged on the street, he was run down and killed. Thus, he came to a sorrowful end, because of this sin in denying God.

CHAPTER 12

"Are you tired, my son?" asked Alma, anxiously watching his son, Shiblon, throw himself upon the ground, beneath a giant tree.

"I am leg weary. I should be ashamed to admit it when you, who are twice my age, seem as fresh as when we left Zarahemla, early this morning," answered the young man.

"I am used to walking and you're not," said Alma, pleasantly, as he seated himself on the trunk of a fallen tree. "I never see you walk, any place, if you can possibly get there on horseback. My missionary labors have kept me walking constantly."

"I suppose you have been in every nook and corner, in all of the Nephite lands," said his son, with admiration.

"Oh, my son," said Alma. "I wish that I were an angel so that I could speak unto all the ends of the earth. I would speak to every soul and cry repentance, with a voice that would shake the earth. But I am a man and I must be content with this human body, the Lord has given me."

"In my opinion, Father, you're a man above all other men. You not only preach the gospel; but live it as well. Every night and morning, I ask God to make me the kind of man you are," said Shiblon, earnestly.

At the sound of his son's words, Alma's heart skipped a beat. This was one of those rare moments that every parent hopes for, but few experience. His son approved of him and wanted to be like him. Suddenly, in that moment of great joy, a painful thought saddened him, for he had a confession to make to his son. Would Shiblon turn away, in hatred, when he heard his father's words? He had meant to tell his sons; but he had put it off, always hoping for just the right time.

"I have a confession to make, which I should have made long ago. Perhaps, when you hear it, you will not longer wish to be like me. I had a wasted youth. I went about the countryside, with the four sons of King Mosiah, bent upon the destruction of the true church of God," said Alma, burying his face in his hands.

"Don't be sad, Father, I know the story," said Shiblon.

"You know? But how?" asked Alma, scarcely believing what he heard.

"My mother told me. She told it so effectively, that my brothers and I grew up, thinking it was one of the most beautiful stories we had ever heard. I like best, the part where the angel descended in a cloud and spoke with a voice of thunder."

"God bless your dear mother. She was wiser

than I. All these years, I have been dreading to tell you," said Alma.

"But why?" asked Shiblon.

"I was afraid that when you knew, you would hate me and I couldn't bear the thought of losing your love and respect," explained Alma, with deep emotion.

"In reality, it made us love you more and gave us a living testimony of the truthfulness of the gospel."

Alma felt that a heavy burden had been lifted from his heart. He, silently, thanked God for giving him such a wonderful wife.

"Thank you, my son. I am a happier man for knowing that you share my secret. As soon as you have rested, we must be on our way, down the mountain, to the waterfall. It is there that I told the others to join us," said Alma.

"We are going to Zoram, aren't we?" asked Shiblon.

"Yes."

"How many are going with us?"

"The three sons of Mosiah, Ammon, Aaron and Omner. I am leaving Himni to take over my duties, in the churches, of Zarahemla. Furthermore, I am taking you and your younger brother, Corianton and two friends," explained Alma.

"But what of Helaman?"

"I am leaving Helaman, my eldest son, to look

after your mother and sisters. We will spend the night at the waterfall and from there, the eight of us will make the journey together, to the land of Zoram."

"I have never been to Zoram. Is it far away?" asked Shiblon, sitting up.

"Yes, my son, it is far away. It lies east of the land of Zarahemla, nearly bordering on the seashore. It is south of the land of Jershon and borders the wilderness which is full of Lamanites."

"Is it true, Father," asked Shiblon, "that the Nephites, who live in the land of Zoram, have turned against God and now worship idols?"

"Yes," replied Alma. "They were once strong believers in God and His son, Jesus Christ; but now, they have fallen into sinful ways and they threaten our security."

"But how can that be?" asked Shiblon.

"The Nephites fear that the Zoramites will make friends with the Lamanites. This would be a means of bringing great loss to the Nephites. Now, my son, we know that preaching the word of God has a way of leading people to the things that are just—yes, it has a more powerful effect upon the minds of people, than the sword or anything else. That is why we mustn't lose any time, in reaching them, with the word of God."

After several days of travel, Alma and his seven missionary companions, reached the land of

Zoram. The first thing they saw was the fine buildings and the beautiful churches. They went inside a church and there they saw a strange thing. In the middle of the church, a high platform was built. It was far above their heads. One at a time, the people of Zoram climbed to the top of the platform and raised their hands above their heads and prayed aloud to a strange god.

"Holy god," they prayed, "you have made it known to us that there is no Christ and we shall be saved while all around us, shall be cast into hell, for which we thank thee, amen."

When Alma and the other missionaries heard these prayers, they were surprised, beyond all measure. Every man offered the same prayer. The place where they prayed was called the Holy Stand. When all the people had said this prayer, they returned to their homes and never spoke of their god until the next week, when it was prayer day again. When Alma saw this, he was very sad. He knew that they were wicked people. Their hearts were set upon gold and silver and all worldly goods. They wore costly clothes. Their fingers were covered with rings and upon their arms were bracelets. About their necks were ornaments of gold and silver and precious gems. Their hair hung down in ringlets. When the Zoramites saw the travel-worn clothing of the missionaries, they drove them out of the church, for only the rich were admitted.

From the church, Alma and his brethren, went their separate ways. They taught the word of God, from house to house and in the streets. The poor people gathered around them, eager to hear again, the word of the Lord. They had been forbidden to worship in the fine churches. They had once kept the commandments of God, for they were Nephites, too. The missionaries taught the poor people repentance and how to seek forgiveness. The poor Zoramites worried because they had no church to worship in. But the missionaries comforted them. They told them that they could worship, in their hearts, and God would hear their prayers and bless them for their faithfulness.

Now, when Alma and his companions had preached the word of God to all the Zoramites, they left Zoram and went over into Jershon, the land of the Anti-Nephi-Lehies. The Nephites called this people by a new name—the people of Ammon.

After the missionaries left Zoram, the rich people grew very angry at the poor, who had accepted the word of God. They drove them out of Zoram. These poor people followed the missionaries to Jershon. They were made welcome by the missionaries and the converted Lamanites. When the ruler, of the Zoramites, heard where they had gone, he sent word, to the people of Ammon, that they must drive his people out of their land. He made many threats against them; but the people of Ammon, were not afraid. They welcomed the poor people of Zoram. They fed them and gave them clothing and lands for their inheritance.

When the Zoramites heard what they had done, their anger was terrible. Immediately, they went into the wilderness and began to mix with the wicked Lamanites. Soon the Zoramites and the Lamanites began to make preparations for war against the people of Ammon and the Nephites.

The people of Ammon gave up the land of Jershon and went over into the land of Melek, so that the armies of the Nephites could use it for a battle ground. Alma and Ammon and their brethren returned to Zarahemla, after bringing many Zoramites to repentance.

When Alma reached home, he saw the sudden look of anxiety, in his wife's eyes.

"Are you ill, my husband?" she asked him, tenderly.

"No, I am not ill—I'm just tired and old," he answered.

Now, Alma's wife had never heard him use the world "old" in connection with himself. He had always had good health and so much energy, that one was apt to take him for a much younger man than he was. Now, as she looked at him, she saw deep lines of worry. His tired, drawn expression, made her count his years. He was, indeed, an old man. However, the next morning, he arose from his bed, looking as though years had fallen away from him overnight. As soon as he had eaten his breakfast, he called Helaman to him.

"My son, Helaman," he said, "I am leaving you the records that have been entrusted to me. You are to keep a record, of this people, upon the plates of Nephi. Here are the brass plates, which contain the records of the holy scriptures. I command you to guard them well. They are to be handed down from generation to generation until they go forth to every nation, kindred, tongue and people. Keep them shining, brightly."

"I shall do as you command. Father, what is this that looks like a compass?" asked Helaman.

"It was given to Lehi, to guide his people to the Promised Land. They called it a ball or director. It has also been known as the Liahona. It worked, for them, when they had faith; but when they doubted God's power, it stood still. And now, my son, see that you take care of these sacred things. Go unto this people and declare the word of God. And now, farewell," said Alma.

Next, he sent for Shiblon and praised him for his faithfulness in the mission field.

"I have had great joy in you," said Alma, "because of your faith and patience among the Zoramites. May the Lord bless your soul and receive you, at the last day, into His Kingdom, to sit down in peace. My son, farewell."

Before he sent for his youngest son, Corianton, he sat for a long time, sick at heart, because of the things he was forced to say to him. When at last, he sent for him, he said:

"Shiblon has set a good example for you; but you did not follow it. You, Corianton, did not listen to my words. You grew proud and boastful of your own strength and wisdom. And this is not all, my son. You have committed a terrible sin in the eyes of the Lord. Go before the Lord, in prayer, and ask His forgiveness. You, as the son of the high priest, should set a good example for the people to follow. Oh, my son, humble yourself and go among the people and preach the word of God. Amen."

The sons of Alma went among the people, teaching them. But, Alma, himself, couldn't rest and he, too, went forth crying repentance to all those who would listen.

CHAPTER 13

In the beginning of the eighteenth year of the reign of the judges, the sound of war echoed and re-echoed throughout all the precious land of promise. The icy fingers of fear reached out and gripped the hearts of all the people. They knew what a terrible thing war was. The Zoramites joined the Lamanites and became Lamanites. Furthermore, they joined forces with the Amalekites, who were a wicked people. The Lamanites gathered their forces, by the thousands, in the land of Zoram.

When the Nephites saw that they were coming to destroy them, they began making preparations for war. They gathered their armies in the land of Jershon. It was the plan of the Nephites to protect their lands, their houses, their wives and children from the hands of their enemies. Above all, they wished to preserve their liberty, so that they might worship God according to their own desires. In this hour of peril, they thought of the black hatred the Lamanites held for their brethren, the Anti-Nephi-Lehies or the people of Ammon, as the Nephites called them. The people of Ammon would not take up arms even to save their lives. Therefore, if the Lamanites came upon them, they would be destroyed. However, the Nephites had made up their minds to protect them at any cost. They gave them lands for their inheritance, outside the battlefield. In return, the people of Ammon gave a large share of their produce to support the army.

The man appointed to be the chief captain over the Nephites was Moroni. Now, the chief captain took command of all the armies of his people. Moroni was only twenty-five years old—a strong, handsome man, loved and respected by all his people. With Moroni leading them, they felt sure of victory. He met the Lamanites in the borders of Jershon. When the armies of the Lamanites saw that the people of Nephi had been prepared with breastplates, arm shields, head shields and dressed in thick clothing, they were seized with terror. The Lamanites were naked, except for a skin, which they wore about their loins. And because of their nakedness, they did not dare to fight them. The Lamanites went into the wilderness. They made a long journey toward the river Sidon, in order to come into the land of Manti and take possession of it, before Moroni knew where they had gone.

But Moroni, being a wise leader, sent spies into the wilderness to watch their camp. He remembered Alma and his prophecies. Therefore, he sent men, to go to Alma and request that he pray to God, and ask Him where the armies of the Nephites should go, to defend themselves, against the Lamanites. Alma did as Moroni requested and the word of the Lord came to him, saying:

"The armies of the Lamanites are marching about the wilderness. They plan to come into the land of Manti, because it is the weakest city of the Nephites."

As soon as Moroni received the message, he knew just what to do. He placed his armies so that they encircled the Lamanites and no matter which way they turned, they found part of Moroni's army. But the Lamanites, seeing that they were surrounded, began fighting fiercely. Since they had double the number of men, it began to look, for a while, like they would win the battle. But Moroni's voice came to his men, saying:

"Fight men, fight! Think of your women and children. Our cause is just because we fight to protect our liberty, our lands and our homes and above all, the right to worship God as we choose. Death would be better than to become slaves of the Lamanites."

When the men heard these words, they fought with new courage. When the Lamanites saw that they were being defeated, terror seized them and they stood helpless before the Nephites.

"Stop!" shouted Moroni. "We have beaten them and there is no need to shed more blood. You know that you are in our hands and we do not wish to kill you. We came only to defend our liberties, not to shed blood or take you as our slaves. The Lord has been good to us and delivered you into our hands.

We shall set you free, because of our religion and our faith in Christ."

Moroni made the Lamanites promise never to come against them, again, in war. When they had made this promise, both the armies of the Lamanites and the Nephites, returned to their own homes. Thus ended the record of Alma, which was written upon the plates of Nephi.

During the golden autumn, in the 19th year of the reign of the judges, Alma came to Helaman and said:

"Do you believe what I have told you about the importance of the records of our fathers?"

"Yes, Father, I believe," said Helaman.

"Do you believe in Jesus Christ, who shall come?" asked Alma, again.

"Yes, I believe all the words you have spoken," said Helaman.

"Will you keep my commandments?" asked Alma.

And Helaman said, "Yes, I will keep your commandments with all my heart."

"You are blessed and the Lord shall prosper you in this land," said Alma. "But I have something to prophesy to you. It must be kept secret until the prophecy is fulfilled. Therefore, write down what I shall tell you."

Helaman did as he was told and this is what he wrote: "I see that this very people, the Nephites, according to the spirit of revelation, in 400 years from the time that Jesus Christ shall come to this land, shall lose their faith. Yes, and there shall be wars, famines and bloodshed, even until the people of Nephi shall be entirely wiped out. This will come true, because they will lose faith in God. They will fall into darkness and all manner of sin. But, if any remain and are not destroyed in that great and terrible day, they will be numbered among the Lamanites. Yes, and they shall become like them—all except a few who shall be called the disciples of the Lord. The Lamanites will hunt these disciples down and slay them."

After Alma had said these things to Helaman, he gave him a blessing. Then he sent for his two other sons and blessed them. Furthermore, he blessed the church and all those who should stand fast in the faith.

That very afternoon, Alma said farewell to his family. He walked out of Zarahemla and took the road that led to Melek. When many days had passed and there was no word from him, his good wife and sons began to worry.

One evening, Alma's wife called her three sons to her and said, "Your father has been gone for the space of many days. I am worried about him."

"But, Mother," said Helaman, "Father has often stayed away, from home, for long periods of time."

"Yes, I know," answered his mother, "but always

before, he sent me messages, telling me where and how he was. This time, there has been no news from him, from any source."

Corianton, who probably loved his mother more tenderly than any of her children, saw the deep lines of worry on her pale face. He was deeply touched and went quickly to her side, placing an arm about her thin shoulders.

"Don't worry, little mother," he said. "We are sure to find him."

She smiled at her youngest son, and said, "Thank you, Corianton. I need all three of you. I want you to organize a searching party. Go into every nook and corner of this great land, and search for your father. We know he set out for Melek. If you do not find him in the Nephite country, search the lands of our enemies."

Alma's sons were only too willing to obey their mother, for they loved their father and respected him, above any other man. In spite of their efforts, winter, spring, summer and fall came again and, still, there was no word of Alma. His children watched their mother grow thin and fade away into a tiny old lady, with eyes that were always searching for her lost Alma. But then, one day, in late autumn, Helaman, Shiblon and Corianton saw a change come over their mother. Her eyes were no longer haunted by searching. There was a shining look about her and one sensed a feeling of quiet peace.

"Mother," asked Shiblon, "have you received good news about Father?"

"No, I have received no news and yet, I have a message for you. You are not to continue the search."

"But why?" asked her sons.

"Because," she answered, "your father is no longer with us. God has taken him home."

"But Mother," said Helaman, sternly, "we have found no evidence of his death or his burial."

"You know that your father was a righteous man."

"Yes, we know this," they answered.

"I believe," said their mother, with quiet devotion, "that God needed Alma. He has taken him up, by the Spirit, or buried him, by His own hands, even as He did Moses. Now the scripture says that the Lord took Moses to Himself and so, I suppose, He has also received Alma, in the Spirit. Therefore, because of this, we know nothing about his death and burial."

Alma's children accepted their mother's belief and the word went forth, throughout all the church, of Alma's reward for his righteous living. With their father as an example, the three sons of Alma went out among all the people of Nephi and preached the word of God. There was great need for teaching the people, because they had become rich and proud of their worldly possessions.

CHAPTER 14

From among the Nephites, came a strong, handsome man, with evil, dark eyes. Amalickiah, for this was the name of the man, loved worldly possessions with all his heart. He wanted to be a rich man more than anything else on earth. At last, he became rich, not because he earned it; but because he learned to trick the vain, proud people. However, after he became wealthy, he was still not satisfied. He wanted power, so that he could control the lives of the people about him. The more he thought of it, the more he liked the idea. He must become their king and after he had become king of the Nephites, he would then find a way to become king of the Lamanites, too.

Amalickiah set to work, immediately, to influence the people. He told the lower judges that they were too good to work under the chief judge and if they would appoint him king, he would place them in charge of the courts of the land. To each group of people, he held out promises and said many flattering things, until they began to believe him. Many of them left the church and soon forgot God's mercy. They, also, forgot to keep the commandments of God and this made them easy prey for the wicked Amalickiah.

When Moroni heard that Amalickiah wanted to be king, he became very angry and said, "This man is dangerous. It is time that all those who believe in Christ, must unite to preserve their liberty."

Then Moroni took off his coat and tore a strip of cloth from it and wrote this message: "In memory of our God, our religion, our freedom, our peace, our wives and our children." When it was written, he fastened it to the end of a pole. Then, putting on his armor, he carried the pole forward. He bowed himself down to the earth and prayed to God, for His blessings of liberty to rest upon his people, so long as there should be a band of Christians to possess the land. When he had poured out his heart to God, he went forth among the people, waving the torn part of his coat. From every direction, people ran to him and offered their services in the cause of freedom.

Now, when Amalickiah saw that most of the people had joined Moroni, he became frightened. He knew that those who joined with him, were doubtful of the justice of their cause and would probably desert him, at any moment. Therefore, he took those who would go with him, and started for the land of Nephi.

When Moroni learned that Amalickiah was headed for the Lamanite territory, he thought it wise to cut them off, before they joined forces with the Lamanites. He ordered his men to bring them back and put Amalickiah to death. They did as they were commanded; but Amalickiah, with a few of his men, escaped and were soon in the land of Nephi.

Never before, had the people of Nephi been so closely united as they were at this time. They worked, unselfishly, for the common good of all the people. Even though, the threat of a Lamanite war hung over them, yet their joy knew no bounds. They kept the Lord's commandments, faithfully, and He poured out rich blessings of peace, happiness and prosperity.

Shortly after Amalickiah fled to Nephi, the land of the Lamanites, Ammon came to Zarahemla. He came to see Moroni. Although, Moroni was many years younger than Ammon, yet they had much in common. When they were together, they forgot the difference in their ages.

"How are your people, the converted Lamanites?" asked Moroni, warmly.

"Oh Moroni," said Ammon, "they are a wonderful people—always rejoicing in the goodness of God. If all the people in this precious land of promise, were as faithful as they are, there would be no war."

"Much of the credit is due you and your three brothers. You spend all your time, reminding them of God's blessings and teaching them in the ways of the Lord."

"I have brought you news," said Ammon. "It seemed so important that I decided to bring it to you myself. It is about Amalickiah."

"Amalickiah?" questioned Moroni.

"Did you know, he is king of the Lamanites?" asked Ammon.

"King of the Lamanites?" repeated Moroni. "Why, that's impossible."

"In the few weeks, he has been in the land of Nephi, he has lied, tricked and murdered his way to the throne. Now, he is king of all the Lamanites, in all their lands. He had his servant, slowly, poison the Lamanite leader of the army. When he was out of the way, Amalickiah took over the leadership and marched to the city of Nephi. When the king came out to meet them, Amalickiah had one of his servants stab the king to death. But, through clever planning, no one knew that he had had any part in the treachery. He told the Lamanites that it was the king's servants, who were responsible for his death. When the servants, of the king, heard these lies, they became frightened and fled to my people, in the land of the Nephites. Knowing that, now, Amalickiah would incite the Lamanites to war against us, I decided you should know of these things."

"Thank you, Ammon," said Moroni. "I will need to speed up our preparations for war. But, tell me, what has become of the Lamanite queen? Has she been murdered?"

"Amalickiah is a clever man and wicked, through and through. With his silver-tongued flattery, he won the heart of the queen and she is now his wife."

"Amazing," was all that Moroni could say, so great was his bewilderment.

Ammon was right, in thinking that Amalickiah would stir up the Lamanites to make war upon the Nephites. At that very moment, he had men appointed to speak to the Lamanites, from their towers. These men told them how they had been robbed and cheated by the Nephites. They kept on, building their hatred, until they were eager to make war upon the Nephites. All Amalickiah's plans were being fulfilled. He was, now, king of the Lamanites and he must become king of the Nephites, too. He gathered a great army, and following Moroni's methods of protecting his men, from arrows and stones, he had them dressed in armor. He pictured, to his men, that soon the Nephites would be their slaves and they would have nothing to do, but live from the labors of the Nephites.

Amalickiah appointed his chief captains from among the Zoramites. They were, in reality, Nephites and they knew, well, the strength of the Nephites and their weakest cities.

At the end of the nineteenth year of the reign of the judges, the Lamanite army moved toward the land of Zarahemla, by way of the wilderness. While Amalickiah had been lying, cheating and murdering his way into power, Moroni, on the other hand, had been preparing the minds of his people to be faithful to the Lord, their God. He began, at once, strengthening his army and building small forts; throwing up banks of earth and placing timbers, on top of the banks, for the protection of his army. He also built walls of stone, to encircle their cities and the borders of their lands. In the weakest places, he stationed a greater number of men. The Nephites kept on working, under Moroni's guidance, until all their lands and their cities were well protected. Moroni gave all his time, preparing to preserve their liberty, their lands, their wives, their children and their peace. He wanted the Nephites to be faithful to God.

Moroni was a strong and mighty man. He hated bloodshed; but he taught the Nephites to defend themselves, against their enemies. He, also, taught them never to give an offense and never to raise the sword, except against an enemy, to preserve their lives. If all men had been, and were, and ever would be like Moroni, the very powers of hell would be shaken forever. The devil would never have a chance to gain power over the hearts of men.

Moroni was a man like Ammon and his brothers and like Alma and his sons. They all preached the word of God and through their labors, the people became humble and served the Lord faithfully. They were brought so close together, through their faith, that for the space of four years, they lived in perfect peace and harmony among themselves. Yet, in spite of this fact, they were compelled to fight with their brethren, the Lamanites. And their wars with the Lamanites never ceased for the space of many years.

Amalickiah sent his Lamanite armies to attack

the re-built city of Ammonihah. This was the wicked city that God destroyed, many years before and the Nephites had just started to re-build it. Amalickiah considered it one of the weakest spots in the Nephite territory. Therefore, he expected little or no trouble in capturing it, and once it had fallen into his hands, he would have a stronghold from which to storm other cities. But a great surprise was in store for him. He hadn't considered the brilliant mind of Moroni or his clever preparations for war. Moroni's wisdom and inspired leadership, gave him the power to forsee the plans and movements of the Lamanites. Amalickiah had no way of knowing how well the lands and cities, of the people of Nephi, were fortified.

When the Lamanites approached the city of Ammonihah, they were amazed to see the deep ditches and the high ridges, of earth, piled up around the city. Suddenly, the Nephites began casting stones and shooting arrows into the unprotected Lamanites, and hundreds of them dropped dead. While, on the other hand, only fifty of the Nephites were wounded. The Lamanites fought wildly, trying to tear down the walls of earth, in order to gain entrance to the city. But, the more they fought, the more terrible their loss became. At last, they fled back, into the wilderness. When Amalickiah heard of their terrible defeat, his face grew dark with anger.

"Moroni will live to regret this day," said Amalickiah. "I shall kill him with my own hands."

Amalickiah soon discovered that this threat could not be accomplished as easily as he thought. Time after time, he sent his armies to attack the Nephite cities; but, each time, they suffered heart-breaking defeats, while the Nephites fought without danger, from behind the ridges of earth.

For the space of four years, the Nephites lived in peace with each other. Although they were compelled to defend themselves against the Lamanites, still, they enjoyed great happiness. Not since Nephi's day, had the people been so united or so faithful to God's commandments. Little did they know that their peace was not to last.

In the twenty-fifth year of the reign of the judges, Nephihah, chief judge over the people of Nephi, died and his son, Pahoran was appointed to take his place. A group of people, claiming to be of royal blood, came to Pahoran and demanded that he alter the law.

"No," said Pahoran, "I shall not alter the law in any respect."

"We," they said, "do not believe in free government. We want a king and we intend to have one."

All those who wanted a king to rule over them, were known as king-men; and those who wanted liberty and freedom, were called freemen. The quarreling, between the two groups, grew very bitter and hostile. When Moroni heard of the uprising, he was deeply grieved for he knew that the Nephite strength lay in their unity. They had fought together to preserve their liberty and the disloyalty of the king-men shocked him, deeply. He loved all his people; but, being a soldier, he knew what dangers lay in rebellion. They must be supressed as quickly as possible. Therefore, he called out his army and sent them forth to battle against the king-men. In a very short time, four thousand of the king-men were slain and their leaders thrown into prison. Those who were left, promised to support and fight for their liberty and freedom.

CHAPTER 15

In the 25th year of the reign of the judges, Moroni stood atop the look-out tower, which gave a view of the great city of Zarahemla and all its border lands. It was the last day of summer and the heat had settled down like a heavy blanket, shutting out every breath of air. But Moroni was unaware of the heat, for he was sad and worried. He was sad because he had to deal, so harshly, with the king-men and because so many of them had been killed. He hated bloodshed; but he knew it was God's will, that the people of Nephi should be free. As leader of the army, it was his duty to preserve their freedom. He was worried because this was a critical time for such trouble to break out, among the people of Nephi. For, behold, Amalickiah had again stirred up the hearts of the Lamanites against the Nephites. He was gathering soldiers from all parts of his land, and arming them and preparing for war. He had sworn to slay Moroni, with his own hands.

Just at that moment, there was a clatter of running feet, coming up the stairway that led to the tower. Turning around, Moroni saw a curly headed child. When the boy reached the landing, he called out:

"Hello, Chief Captain, Moroni!"

"Hello, there! Who are you?" asked Moroni, smiling at the small boy.

"I'm nobody important; but I bring you a secret message," said the boy with pride.

"If you were chosen," said Moroni, "to bring me a secret message, then you must be someone very important—someone I can trust."

"Yes sir, everyone knows that I can be trusted. My name is Helaman, son of Helaman and grandson of Alma," said the boy, boasting a little.

"Well, my lad, you have a great deal to live up to. Your grandfather was a great man, in the ways of the Lord, and your father is following in his footsteps," said Moroni, kindly.

"I know that, sir," said the boy, politely. "I am trying to be like them."

"Fine," said Moroni. "And now, tell me, what is this message that is so important and secret?"

"Teancum, leader of one of your armies, sent me to tell you that, while you have been putting down rebellion, here at home, the Lamanites have come into the land of Moroni, which borders on the seashore. Amalickiah has driven the people out and killed many of them. He has taken over the city."

Now, Moroni had been afraid that this very thing would happen. Nevertheless, the news came as a shock. He closed his eyes and prayed that God would be merciful to his people, whom the Lamanites had captured. Suddenly, he looked at young Helaman, searchingly. He seemed to be an honest child; but still, there was something strange about his story.

"Helaman," said Moroni, "the city of Moroni lies far to the East. So great a distance, in fact, that a small boy, like you, couldn't possibly travel so far."

"Oh, sir," said Helaman, 'the message was relayed to me. You see, sir, there are a number of men stationed at different places along the way and it is their duty to get the messages through to you. I am stationed only a few miles out of Zarahemla. You see, Sir, I am one of the younger men."

Moroni smiled at the manly little fellow, who was trying so hard to be grownup.

"Take this message to Teancum and Lehi: Say that I will join them, as soon as possible."

"Yes, sir," said Helaman and was off like the wind.

Before Moroni could gather his army and move them from the west to the eastern seashore, several of the Nephite cities fell into the hands of the Lamanites. Amalickiah, the wicked king of the Lamanites, lost his life, and Ammoron, his brother, became king in his place. When the Nephites lost one of their cities, it seemed impossible to retake it again; because they were all so well protected with walls of stone and great ridges of earth. But, to Moroni, nothing seemed impossible. His faith in God was firm and strong and he knew that his cause was just

—the cause of freedom. As soon as he arrived, he saw clearly that they would have to lure the Lamanites out of the cities in order to take them. He accomplished this through cunning and daring and Mulek was retaken and a great victory was won.

As the fighting continued week after week and month after month, the Nephites captured a large number of prisoners. Moroni ordered his men to preserve the lives of the prisoners, so that they might exchange them for Nephites, who had fallen into Lamanite hands. In the 29th year of the reign of the judges, Ammoron sent word to Moroni, telling him he wished to exchange prisoners. Moroni was overjoyed at this news and sent a message to Ammoron, saying:

"It is you and your brother, Amalickiah, who came against my people in war. If you do not repent and withdraw your armies into your own lands, you will bring down the anger of that God, whom you have rejected, and He will destroy you. I will not exchange prisoners, except on condition that you will deliver, to us, a man, his wife and his children for one prisoner. Now, behold, if you do not agree to this, I will come against you with my armies; yes, I will do more than that, I will arm my women and children and I will follow you to your own lands, which is the land of our first inheritance. I will give you battle until you are destroyed from off the face of the earth."

When Ammoron received Moroni's message, he was very angry and he wrote him, saying:

"I am Ammoron, a descendant of Zoram. But now, I am a bold Lamanite. Your fathers did rob the Lamanites of the right to govern you. If you will lay down your arms and subject yourselves to be governed, by those to whom the government rightly belongs, then I will cause my people to lay down their arms. You say, we have rejected your God; but we know no such God and neither do you. If there is such a being, then He has made us, as well as you. If there is a devil and a hell, perhaps, He will send you to dwell with my brother, whom you have murdered. We have waged this war to obtain the Lamanite's right to the government. And, now, I close my letter to Moroni."

When Moroni received this message, he was very angry. He knew that Ammoron was aware of his lies.

"I will not exchange prisoners with Ammoron," said Moroni, fiercely. "Now, I know that my people are held in the city of Gid, under heavy Lamanite guard."

Moroni stopped speaking and sat, lost in deep study. His men, knowing he wished to be alone, left the room quietly. Several minutes passed and then, a light knock came upon his door. But Moroni had no eyes or ears for anyone or anything. The knock came again and then, without waiting, the door opened and a tall, young boy entered the room and stood watching Moroni, with profound respect.

At last, Moroni spoke aloud, to himself. "What shall I do?"

"Ask God," said the boy.

Moroni was startled at the sound of a strange voice and said, sternly, "Who are you and what are you doing here?"

"I am Helaman, son of Helaman and—"

"And grandson of Alma," finished Moroni, smiling.

"Then you remember me?" asked Helaman, surprised.

"Yes, indeed I do, although it has been a long time since I last saw you. You have been growing so fast, I didn't know you at first," said Moroni.

"I can do a man's work now," said young Helaman, proudly.

"What can I do for you?" asked Moroni, kindly; but still aware that his time was precious.

"I have come here, sir, to offer my services in our fight for freedom. Shall we pray together?"

Moroni sat amazed at this boy, who always surprised him with his courage and faith. Without saying another word, Moroni knelt down with Helaman and asked God for guidance. While Moroni prayed, God's voice came to his mind and suggested a way to free the Nephite captives.

"Helaman, will you search among my people for a man who is a descendant of Laman, son of Lehi?"

"Yes," said Helaman, happy to be of service.

In a short time, Helaman returned, bringing a Lamanite with him.

"What is your name?" asked Moroni.

"My name is Laman and I am a descendant of the first Laman, who came out of Jerusalem 537 years ago."

"Good," said Moroni. "But how did you come to join my forces? Do you believe in freedom for all the children of men?"

"I do, now, sir. But that is not why I am here. When the wicked Amalickiah had my king murdered, he blamed me and the king's other servants. We were forced to flee out of our lands. However, my coming among your people and my people, the Anti-Nephi-Lehies, was a great blessing to me. Here, I learned of the coming of Jesus Christ. I am deeply grateful for this knowledge and, now, if I can be of any use, I am here to serve you."

While Laman talked, Moroni studied him carefully. He had the feeling that here was a man, good and true. The Nephite and the Lamanite were united in common brotherhood. Moroni outlined his plan to Laman and when he was through, the two men clasped hands in warm friendship.

That evening, under cover of darkness, Laman,

with a small number of his men, set out for the city
of Gid, where the Lamanites held the Nephite prisoners. Within a few feet of the city gates, suddenly, a
voice cried out on the still night air:

"Halt! Who goes there?"

"Fear not for, behold, I am a Lamanite," said
Laman. "We have escaped from the Nephites while
they sleep. We have taken their wine and brought
it with us."

The Lamanites were very fond of wine and,
especially, wine made by the Nephites, so when they
heard Laman's words, they received him with joy.

"Give us your wine, that we may drink, for we
are very weary."

But Laman teased them by saying, "Let us
keep our wine, until we go against the Nephites in
battle."

But these words only made the Lamanites more
anxious than ever, to drink the wine and they said,
"We are weary. Let us drink the wine, now, and by
and by, we will be given our wine which will strength-
en us for the battle."

"Here it is," said Laman. "Drink it if you wish."

They drank the wine freely and smacked their
lips over its pleasant taste. Now, the wine was
strong, on purpose, so that the Lamanites would fall
into a deep, drunken sleep. They drank and drank
and made merry. When they were all asleep, Laman

and his men, returned to Moroni and told him what had happened.

"You have done well," said Moroni. "And now, my men will carry weapons of war to the city of Gid and while the Lamanites sleep, we will arm the Nephite prisoners. Yes, even the women and children, who are able to use a weapon of war, will be armed."

The men moved quietly and swiftly to the city of Gid, where they gave the weapons to the Nephite prisoners in profound silence. Not a single Lamanite awakened. Now, the Nephites could have slain the drunken Lamanites, for they lay in a deep sleep. But Moroni had ordered his men to spare them. He had no desire to shed the blood of his enemies—only to free his people. He had obtained just what he wanted. Next morning, when the Lamanites awakened, they were shocked to find that they were surrounded by Nephites outside the city and by their prisoners from within. Moroni ordered them to lay down their weapons and when this was done, he took them prisoner.

After Moroni had everything well in hand, he sent for Laman and said, "You played your part wonderfully well and I want to thank you from the bottom of my heart."

It was a well known fact, that Moroni gave his compliments sparingly and only to the few, who really deserved them. Now, Laman knew this and when he heard Moroni's words and felt his warm hand clasp, he straightened his shoulders, with pride.

"Thank you," said Laman. "I believe the Lord, our God, is well pleased with the work you did last night. You set the Nephite prisoners free and captured the Lamanite guards, without losing a single soul. You are the wisest and greatest man I ever knew."

"Any wisdom or success I may have, is given me by the mercy of God," said Moroni, humbly. "Laman my friend, I am sick unto death, of war and bloodshed. I wish we were done with it, so that we might turn our energies to preparing the minds of the people, for the coming of Christ."

"Is he coming soon?" asked Laman, eagerly.

"I don't know the time or place of His coming; but I believe it will be soon. Perhaps, some of our children will live to see Him. Laman, I pray God that we may be worthy of His great sacrifice."

"Amen," was all Laman could say, so deep was his emotion.

And thus ended the 29th year of the reign of the judges.